between earth and space

between earth

and space / Clyde Orr, Jr.

The Macmillan Company   New York   1960

Fourth Printing 1960

Library of Congress catalog card number: 59-5640

The Macmillan Company, New York
Brett-Macmillan Ltd., Galt, Ontario

Printed in the United States of America

preface

IDEOLOGIES, FADS, fashions, wars, and threats of wars shape the immediate course of human events. The long-range future of society, however, will be dictated largely by the success with which mankind solves three fundamental problems: problems that are neither political nor sociological in nature, but rather are scientific.

The first is energy with which to power our mills and factories, to supply our means of transportation, to keep us warm or cool. Our present fuels, including atomic ones, are not renewable. We must eventually harness a truly infinite source of energy, perhaps the sun, or risk an Industrial Revolution in reverse, with dreadful consequences. The second major problem to be faced is fuller utilization and more careful husbandry of all our natural resources. A spectacular surge in the world's population in coming generations is inevitable, bringing with it a greatly increased demand for material things. Our water supply, already dangerously low in many areas, must be maintained and even augmented, perhaps by making sea water potable. For years we have been using only the highest-grade ores, but in the future we must utilize some poorer raw materials and find substitutes for others. Finally, the third problem is the maintenance and improvement of our environment—in short, making the earth a more pleasant and suitable habitat.

Clearly, the last problem encompasses our earth's atmosphere; for weather phenomena, climatic changes, contaminating gases, aerial warfare, and the like determine the degree to which our natural environment serves our needs. Though not so obviously, the other problems also relate to our atmosphere. Either we must tap a greater portion of the sun's energy that manages to pass through the atmosphere to us, or we must harness it unsullied beyond the atmosphere. And in the last analysis, the atmosphere is our most precious natural resource; for in addition to being a necessity for all living things, its gases permit us to refine our metal ores, run our automobiles, and carry on a hundred and one ordinary daily activities.

Today, to an extent not even imagined a few years ago, modern man is acquiring knowledge of and control over the processes of nature. Soon, perhaps too soon, we will have the power to make the earth truly our home, to make it an environment adapted to our desires. But if care and judgment are not exercised, we can also defile it to such an extent that life will become impossible. This book attempts to present the conditions of our atmospheric habitat as now known, to indicate the directions the attacks on nature's secrets are taking, and to suggest a bit of the future.

It may be helpful to know in advance the plan of the work. The opening chapter presents a general introduction and a preview of what is to follow. The second chapter attempts to show how the earth's atmosphere came into being. Chapter 3 considers the regions miles above the earth. In the following three chapters, we will come back to earth, as it were, to deal with the wind, storm, rain, snow, hail, and lightning. Another chapter deals with the effects of solid, though finely divided, matter such as dust and pollen grains which we find in the air. One chapter discusses aesthetic effects of the atmosphere, the color of the sky and clouds, sunsets and rainbows. One deals with sound, vibrations in the air. Three chapters consider weather, weather modifications, and climate. Pollution of the air is treated in one chapter. The final chapter reaches upward again to present the challenge of supersonic flight beyond the stratosphere and thence into space itself.

In sum, this book is intended to give the inquiring reader a fuller knowledge of the wonderful airy realm. It perhaps may be found timely, serving as a basis for the evaluation of current and future scientific discoveries. If it proves other than interesting, it is not the fault of the subject; for, as Ruskin wrote, the sky is "sometimes gentle, sometimes capricious, sometimes awful, never the same for two moments together; almost human in its passions, almost spiritual in its tenderness, almost Divine in its infinity."

My interest in the atmosphere stems from my association with the late Professor J. M. DallaValle, the scientific discussions we had, and the research investigations we undertook together. To him belongs my sincere gratitude for encouragement and generous assistance. Many others have contributed from their specialized knowledge. In this connection I wish particularly to thank my colleagues at Georgia Tech and associates within Air Force research organizations. Individuals, companies, and agencies supplying the illustrative material are also acknowledged for their efforts. Finally, words cannot express the debt I owe my wife for her understanding patience, tireless reading, and invaluable suggestions in the interest of clarity.

The information contained herein was compiled from many sources: books, technical journals, magazine articles, trade publications, newspaper stories, lectures, and private communications. It would not be possible to list them all. Works from which supplementary information may be obtained or which are especially recommended for general reading are given in the Selected Reading List.

C.O.

Atlanta, Georgia
July, 1958

contents

1 the airy domain

*A light, a glory, a fair luminous cloud
enveloping the Earth.*

SAMUEL TAYLOR COLERIDGE

OUR EARTH is a globe about eight thousand miles in diameter. Its interior is a hot, molten mass. Only a very thin crust a few dozen miles in depth forms the surface, a crust thinner in comparison than an eggshell. Three-quarters of the earth's surface is covered, in turn, by water. Finally, the water oceans and the land alike are surmounted by an ocean of air, the atmosphere.

In this airy realm we have our being; in it we move about as fishes move about the sea; our activities are subject to its whims; our lives, as well as those of every living thing, depend upon it. They depend not only upon its presence but also upon its conditions being maintained within narrow limits. Were there no atmosphere, the earth would be sterile, without weather, cloud, or multicolored sunset. No sound would disturb the deathly quiet. Exposed to the full fury of the sun and the intense cold of space, the earth would be seared on one side and frozen on the other. Its surface would be pitted with the scars of colliding meteorites.

Since time immemorial man has of necessity observed atmospheric phenomena. Primitive man, seeing that the earth was bathed with rain and warmed by the sun so that she might bring forth an abundance of plant and animal life to satisfy his needs, naturally ascribed to the elements the attributes of gods who wisely arranged his abode. We now know that the earth actually was not designed for man but that he is its child, a product of the evolutionary process that fashioned all species. We were molded to suit the earth, not the other way round. It is not by chance that the earth, wearing a blanket of air, spins through space at exactly the right distance from the sun to be neither too hot nor too cold. It did not just happen that the atmosphere is of the right composition and amount to cut out those portions of the sun's rays that would destroy life and to let pass the life-sustaining parts; that the earth has an abundance of water, which is picked up in the atmosphere and spread over the land; or that the air is exactly the right combination of oxygen and nitrogen for the needs of our bodies. We developed to require these conditions because the conditions themselves shaped our development.

As we know, the atmosphere pervades everything on earth. We find it whether we descend the deepest mine or climb the highest mountain. It is present at the poles and at the equator. Containers that are said to be empty are actually full unless they have been evacuated with special pumps and sealed. The atmosphere extends in ever diminishing quantities hundreds of miles overhead. Even there it does not come to a definite end. It thins out gradually; there is no definite point at which there is air and beyond which there is only empty space.

Casually we think of air as being weightless, the essence of nothingness. But our atmosphere is not in fact light. A bathtub of it weighs nearly two pounds; the air in an ordinary living room, if compressed into a container the size of a suitcase, could be lifted by only the strongest men; a tank thirty feet square and thirty feet high contains a ton of air. Altogether, there are about five million billion tons of it, or roughly two million tons for each inhabitant of the earth; if it were compressed to the density of steel it would form a plate of armor forty-nine inches thick all over the globe. Every square inch of the earth's surface is pressed upon by nearly fifteen pounds of air. The air we carry on our shoulders weighs more than a thousand pounds. We are unaware of the pressure and are not crushed by it simply because our blood and the tissue of our bodies are saturated with air and exert a pressure outward equal to the atmospheric pressure pushing inward on us. By the same principle the deep-sea fish is undisturbed by the tremendous pressure of the miles-high mass of water above it.

The air is not, however, merely a static mass pressing upon us. Every thimbleful of it is composed of tremendous numbers of entities called molecules, which are darting hither and thither at fantastic speeds, colliding with each other and rebounding only to collide again. Every cubic inch of air contains about 490 billion billion molecules, and with every breath we draw in something like 10,000 billion billion of them. At ordinary temperatures an average molecule is moving at jet-plane speed; yet it travels a zigzag course, colliding every few millionths of an inch with one of its neighbors. In reality, what we call atmospheric pressure is just the sum total of the impacts of all molecules that are colliding every instant with a surface—for example, the skin of our hands. These are the impacts that amount to nearly fifteen pounds on each square inch of our bodies.

All molecules of the air are not alike; actually this invisible medium is a brew of many elements, some abundant, some rare, some active, and others inert. A few are deadly in sufficient concentration; a few others are essential; and still others are decidedly indifferent. Through the stirring of winds and the fantastic motion of its individual molecules, the air anywhere is very nearly the same as the air anywhere else. Excluding water vapor, which occurs mostly at relatively low altitudes in varying amounts depending on the weather, a little more than 78 per cent of the air is the element called nitrogen. Oxygen makes up nearly 21 per cent, while carbon dioxide, argon, neon, krypton, zenon, helium, radon, and traces of others that arise largely from man's activities compose the other 1 per cent.

In endlessly repeated cycles the three gases first mentioned—nitrogen, oxygen, and carbon dioxide—pass between the unstable organic world and the enduring equilibrium of inorganic nature. Through diversified processes they unite in a majestic partnership that keeps solvent the living economy of the earth. The most abundant element, nitrogen, is a paradox for mankind; in the midst of plenty of it we border on poverty. Chemically inactive, nitrogen enters into combinations with other elements only under extreme duress, yet all living things on this planet, both animal and vegetable, must have it in their food. Because it is so difficult to incorporate this element into foodstuffs, a large share of the world's back-breaking labor must be devoted simply to conserving the relatively small amounts that are captured and fixed in the soil. However, were it less reluctant to unite with other elements, we would be in ever more difficult straits. In combination with the waters of the oceans it could form nitric acid and make our position intolerable.

As nature handles nitrogen, it is jarred out of its sluggishness by the energetic match-making of lightning and wooed by tiny bacteriological organisms in soil and water. High in the atmosphere the former weds small amounts of nitrogen to oxygen, forming nitrogen oxides, and nitrogen to hydrogen from water vapor, producing ammonia; these compounds, washed down by the rain, amount to from one to nine pounds per acre each year and are an important source of the earth's continuing fertility. The latter, organisms called nitrogen fixers and nitrifiers, combine free nitrogen into organic compounds suitable for both animal and plant foods. Still other organisms, denitrifiers, decompose dead organisms, returning nitrogen to the air from whence it must be wrung again.

This continual leakage of nitrogen into the atmosphere poses a survival problem for all living things on the earth. At present we are almost completely dependent on the nitrogen-fixing organisms to recombine nitrogen into plant and animal food. Our best efforts to reverse the nitrogen drain so far have been expensive and have succeeded only in preparing some of the simplest compounds.

Oxygen, unlike nitrogen, is highly reactive. It is responsible for the rusting of metals, it causes the inner surface of an apple to turn brown after a few moments of exposure, and it is the substance that keeps a birthday candle burning. It keeps also the poetic "fire of life" going; for, as a stove requires oxygen to support the combustion of its fuel, so our bodies must have oxygen with which to "burn" the carbon, hydrogen, and nitrogen of our food to water, urea, and carbon dioxide.

Carbon dioxide's story is in part the reverse of oxygen's. Green vegetation in the presence of sunlight takes carbon dioxide from the air and by means of a near-miraculous process called photosynthesis releases oxygen, the carbon going into the woody structure. As an example, one acre of beech forest removes about two thousand pounds of carbon dioxide annually and returns to the atmosphere nearly fifteen hundred pounds of pure oxygen. Altogether the plants of the world in a year's time consume nearly 550 billion tons of carbon dioxide and release 400 billion tons of oxygen. When vegetation decays or is burned its carbon is reconverted into carbon dioxide and escapes into the air. Estimates indicate that atmospheric carbon dioxide passes through one complete cycle on an average of every two to three years. Oxygen, being more plentiful, catches a tour of duty in the realm of organic matter every three thousand years, but reluctant nitrogen evades entanglements usually for one hundred million years. Some of the nitrogen molecules we find in our food today may not have appeared in any other organic combination since long before the reign of the dinosaurs.

Carbon dioxide is also continuously being added to the air through volcanic action and from mineral springs, as well as by the decaying of organic matter, the combustion of fuels, and the respiration of men and animals. It is just as continuously being taken from the air by certain rocks of the earth's crust and the waters of the oceans. At present, some fifty times more carbon dioxide is dissolved in the oceans than is present in the air, the air currently containing only about thirty-three one-thousandths of 1 per cent of this gas. The last half-century has seen an accelerated production of carbon dioxide from the combustion of fuels and from other industrial activities, and a small increase in its quantity has been detected. Some observers see as a result a small, yet significant, world-wide temperature rise, which comes about through a peculiar property of carbon dioxide that enables the earth to retain somewhat more of the sun's energy than it would otherwise.

Of all the rarer gases in the atmosphere, including carbon dioxide, argon is by far the most prevalent. It alone accounts for about 93 per cent of the total 1 per cent of such gases. But argon, neon, krypton, and zenon are quite inert, and as far as is known they play no part in our well-being; they are most familiar as the brilliant color producers of so-called neon signs. Helium too is inert, and is found free in only minute amounts. As a filler for dirigibles and other lighter-than-air balloons, it is not recovered from the air but is extracted from certain gas-producing wells in this country. Radon, as the name suggests, is a product of the disintegrating of radium; it is found in all the air in a total quantity of only a few ounces. Since it too disintegrates, one of its products being helium, it contributes some of the latter but only an insignificant amount.

Water in its invisible gaseous or vapor state is always present in the atmosphere near the earth. Its quantity is subject to wide fluctuation, for at any temperature the air can hold only so much water vapor and no more. Normally this amount is only about a ten-day supply; consequently if evaporation from the seas, rivers, and lakes should cease, all plant and animal life would soon perish from thirst. When the air's temperature is high, lots of water is usually present too, particularly if a large body of water is nearby. But if the temperature drops, a part of the air's permissible water burden must be dropped; this release takes the form of rain, hail, snow, dew, or fog. Weather is thus largely a product of the trials and tribulations of water vapor.

But neither water to become vapor nor heat to evaporate it are uniformly distributed about our planet, so weather is a jumble of complicated phenomena, many of which have so far eluded scientific delving. It is known, however, that the tropical and subtropical areas of the earth absorb much more heat from the sun than do other regions, and that winds, some dry and cold and others hot and loaded with water vapor, derive from the attempt to distribute this heat more or less uniformly about the world. The process is not always orderly because the energy involved is astoundingly large, each one and one-half square miles of the earth receiving daily, on the average, energy from the sun equivalent to one Hiroshima-type atom bomb. Violent thunderstorms, tornadoes, and hurricanes thus develop during the energy's dissipation.

The sun radiates more than the heat and light so familiar to us. Its ultraviolet radiation would be lethal were it not for the atmosphere's acting as a filter to let through, ordinarily, only enough to give us a nice suntan. The atmosphere is also a shield protecting us from a hail of tiny meteors and penetrating, primary cosmic rays. Looking at it another way, the air is our major natural resource. The coal and petroleum we now take from the ground is largely carbon, which in past ages was extracted by plants from the air. Our use of these materials today would cease if we could not burn them with the oxygen of the air. We could not recover metallic iron, copper, zinc, or any of the common metals if we did not have atmospheric oxygen to feed our smelting furnaces.

Clearly, without any of a great many phenomena that involve the atmosphere, we could not survive. Assuming that we could live somehow in the absence of an atmosphere, we would find our environment vastly changed. The sky would be eternally black, and objects on earth would be either brilliantly illuminated by the sun or hidden in inky shadows, for the earth's gaseous envelope, by diffusing sunlight, makes possible the deep blue of the sky, inspiring dawns and sunsets, auroral displays, and the other majestic shows of nature. Without an atmosphere existence would be deathly silent. The tiny air molecules by their rapid back-and-forth darting and by their collisions relay to the membranes of our ears the fact that the air has been agitated. The disturbing object may be an airplane propeller, a jack hammer, or a violin string producing a note from a Beethoven symphony, but the mechanism of sound propagation is the same.

There are tides in the atmosphere just as in the water oceans. Though the movement is imperceptible to our senses, the ocean of air heaves and billows under a wave of atmospheric pressure that runs around the earth twice daily. To detect this tidal motion requires infinite pains and sensitive instruments, for irregular winds and daily heating by the sun all but obliterate its pattern. But despite detection difficulties, atmospheric tides are by no means trivial. Their greatest service is in counteracting the drag of the water ocean tides on the earth's rotation.

For many years it has been recognized that oceanic tides breaking against the continents produce a force that must extract energy from the earth's rotation unless counteracted in some way. Lacking knowledge of any opposing mechanism, the tacit assumption was made that the earth was slowing down, that our days were gradually lengthening, and that only by chance did twenty-four hours happen to be their present length. New information about atmospheric tides changes the picture; our day's length actually represents a balance brought about by the braking of oceanic tides and a speed-up due to atmospheric tides. This being the case, there likely has been little change in the day's length in millions of years and there is no reason to expect a shift in the foreseeable future.

How one tide can be a drag on rotation while another gives an assist is difficult to explain, but basically the answer is familiar to everyone. Spacing his pushes at proper intervals, one boy can give another a very high ride in a swing, but pushes of equal force can stop the swing if timed in a different manner. In the playground through which our earth romps its most influential companions are the sun and the moon. The gravitational force of the moon, asserted through the oceanic tides, is primarily a drag on our planet's rotation; but the sun's force, applied via atmospheric tides, is phased to give a small daily push. Together the two forces have established an equilibrium; a constant period of rotation for our earth is the result.

Whether or not one revels in the beauty of the sky, whether one's livelihood fluctuates with weather conditions or whether one lives in big-city surroundings shielded almost continuously from the elements, he can no more escape being influenced by atmospheric phenomena than could a cave man. Our ability to get work done, a plane's to take off with a load, and a baseball's to curve can be quite different on a hot, humid day and a cool, dry one. In many localities pollution of the air is a problem that begs for solution, yet in all probability the situation will grow worse before sufficient incentive is aroused to force control of our gaseous wastes. The atmosphere is a broad commercial highway as well as a potential battleground of unlimited horizontal and vertical extent. In it may rage combat of the future between machines maneuvering at terrific speeds but controlled by men on the ground. It could become instead the medium for waging an entirely different kind of warfare—warfare without sudden, shattering death and destruction but completely annihilating nevertheless. Invisible radioactivity could diffuse the atmosphere to such an extent that all offspring would become monsters, leading eventually to the disappearance of the species. Odorless, colorless, and relatively cheap gases exist that are so deadly that mere contact with the skin can be fatal. Gases also exist that do not kill but simply sicken, destroying temporarily the will to resist. Disease germs could be spread through the air that would wipe out a people, or that would kill millions of sheep and cattle, thus depriving the people of meat, wool, and hides. Spores that would kill wheat, rice, corn, barley, and rye likewise could be scattered to destroy the sources of bread. It is well within the realm of possibility that from a cloud drifting silently across the sky could come a blighting of the grain, a sickening of the people, a poisoning of the animals, or the polluting of a water supply.

On a more pleasant note, weather and climate are in for changes. Not only will tomorrow's forecast be more accurate, but artificially controlling some aspects of the weather—producing rain, preventing hail, mitigating thunderstorms—is also a possibility presaging great changes. Economic, recreational, and even international affairs are sure to be affected when this development is exploited to the fullest. Great benefits for humanity will result if losses of life and property from thunderstorms only can be reduced. Yet even deserts may be made to bloom again someday by manipulation of rain clouds.

And this is only the beginning. Man, in his striving for the unknown, is already reaching outward toward space itself. But before this greatest of all conquests can come to pass, man must learn to live in the upper regions of our atmosphere as well as to navigate them. Neither task will be easy, for there he will encounter conditions more foreign to his experience than anything imagined a few years ago. But attempt it he must, and conquer it eventually he will.

2 from the beginning

Soon as the evening shades prevail,
The moon takes up the wondrous tale,
And nightly to the listening earth
Repeats the story of her birth;
While all the stars that round her burn,
And all the planets in their turn
Confirm the tidings as they roll,
And spread the truth from pole to pole.

JOSEPH ADDISON

ALL THINGS have a beginning. Some are observed and documented; others are vague and impalpable. The beginning of our earth's atmosphere falls into the latter category, and there many of its stages of development will ever remain, for mankind has witnessed, relatively speaking, only the last few minutes of the earth's existence. We need not despair, however, for there is much that can be learned without benefit of an observer. We have gained a partial understanding of the structure of the atom without ever having seen one. We know how large the earth is and what it weighs, although we have neither put a tape measure around it nor placed it on a balance. We can do as much with the atmosphere. Knowledge acquired through many sciences, when woven together, provides a reasonable account of much of the atmosphere's history.

Our earth's atmosphere is a product of the whole process of

11

creation and subsequent geologic events beginning in the far-distant past and continuing to the present moment. To unravel the mysteries of atmospheric origin we must use, then, such evidence as we are able to find today in the stars overhead and in the rocks under our feet. We must first examine the present state of affairs of our earth and the universe in general. As far as is known, our earth with its particular envelope of gases is unique in the universe, although bodies such as our earth are anything but rare.

An old rhyme goes, "Big fleas have little fleas upon their backs to bite 'em, And little fleas have lesser fleas, and so ad infinitum." Geometrically speaking, this is a rather good description of the make-up of the universe as revealed by modern cosmology. Our earth, called a planet, is circled by the moon, while the earth, along with eight other major planets and many minor ones, revolves about a sun. Our sun, in turn, revolves with several billion other suns, most of which probably have planets circling them, in an assemblage of suns (really stars) called a galaxy. Our galaxy, moving through space like a swarm of bees through the summer air, is but one of at least one billion other galaxies composing our universe. Only four of our sun's planets are smaller than the earth, and the largest, Jupiter, is eleven times greater in diameter. Our sun is an average-sized star, yet it is 332,000 times more massive than the earth, and our galaxy is only of average size as galaxies go. As if this were not sufficiently perplexing, all galaxies seem to be running away from each other as children run from the "it" in a game of tag. In short, the universe appears to be expanding.

Discounting elements such as those man has recently produced in atomic piles and by nuclear bombardment, all the earth, all the stars, and the vast array of galaxies are fashioned from ninety-two elements. It would be far outside our subject to explain here how this has been established, but it will suffice to say that the composition of the stars and galaxies is determined by analysis of the light we receive from them. Although all cosmic bodies do not have equal amounts of each element, the universe as a whole is about 90 per cent hydrogen and 9 per cent helium, both very light gases.

Carbon, nitrogen, and oxygen are next in abundance, in that order. The metallic elements, particularly iron, silicon, magnesium, calcium, aluminum, sodium, and potassium, which comprise a large fraction of the earth, are cosmically quite rare. The heavy elements, such as lead, gold, platinum, uranium, and thorium, are extremely rare. Since neither the earth nor its atmosphere contains significant fractions of hydrogen and helium, our earth must have undergone numerous evolutionary stages.

At present there are two main theories of how the universe came into being and why it is predominantly a hydrogen universe. Neither specifically acknowledges divine intervention; yet, contrary to popular opinion, the concept is not dogmatically excluded. The fact is, we simply do not know. The first holds that the universe was produced from, or was at least extensively reorganized by, a cataclysmal upheaval, not unlike our latest hydrogen bomb explosions, that occurred at least four billion years ago. According to this theory—and there are many observable facts that are explained by it—the matter resulting from the explosion must have been mostly the gases hydrogen and helium with bits of solid matter dispersed therein. From these fragments and gases, the stars, the planets, our earth, and the moon were formed while flying away from the initial upheaval.

The second theory postulates the continuous creation of matter, the new matter filling the void left by the expansion of matter already created. To satisfy the requirements of this theory, only one new hydrogen atom would have to be created in a space the size of the Empire State Building in about ten thousand years. Other atoms, being more complicated than hydrogen, would be formed at a correspondingly slower rate. While a process by which this creation of matter might occur is unknown, scientists can certainly be excused for not having detected it yet if it does happen.

Whatever the mode of formation, a period when the universe was mostly uniformly distributed gases is indicated, and a universe of gas would surely have been unstable. The great British astronomer Sir James Jeans showed that a gas uniformly filling an unlimited space is bound to break up into separate "gas balls" with empty space between them. We believe that the primordial gas, not unlike the curling smoke that rises from a cigarette, broke into gigantic, though lesser, gas balls, which went their separate ways. These balls of gas formed the galaxies. The stars originated from a secondary condensation within the galactic gas balls, forming smaller stellar gas balls. During the secondary condensation, the heavier gases and particles gravitated to the center of the mass. Centrifugal force due to rotation kept other gases and particles outside as a close-fitting, flattened ring or disk, probably something like that which may be observed today about the planet Saturn. It is probable that as much as 99 per cent of this band was gaseous hydrogen and helium and only 1 per cent was solid particles, perhaps particles of silicates (rock), iron oxide (rust), ice crystals, and others. Nevertheless, the particles of this disk collided frequently with one another, with the result that aggregates grew ever larger and larger. The larger chunks of material captured the smaller ones by collision until the former found themselves moving in nearly empty space. The major portion of the mass meanwhile continued to contract and, as a result of tremendous gravitational forces, became heated to the threshold temperature for nuclear reaction, some forty million degrees on our Fahrenheit scale. When this point was reached the liberation of nuclear energy started, the center mass became a brilliant star, a sun, and the outer aggregates of material took on the role of planets. The fires of heaven were kindled; the universe was illuminated.

Before we reconstruct the evolutionary steps through which the earth's atmosphere then proceeded, let us consider again what makes an atmosphere. As we saw in the first chapter, it is a gas (the clouds, dust, and smoke may be neglected for the present); and a gas is an elastic assemblage of molecules. Each molecule is in a state of perpetual motion, moving in a straight line until colliding with another molecule. Not all molecules of a gas are equally energetic at any given temperature and pressure. At the temperature of freezing water, the average molecule of hydrogen gas moves with a speed of a little more than one mile per second, but an appreciable fraction of the molecules moves with speeds five times that great. At a temperature of 1800 degrees Fahrenheit, the average molecular speed jumps to two and one-half miles per second, with the velocities of many molecules at any one time exceeding ten miles per second. We are concerned here with these speeds and temperatures simply because we know the velocity any body, whether a rocket or a molecule, must have in order to escape from the earth. This so-called escape velocity is seven and one-tenth miles per second. If a rocket attains this speed vertically upward, it can leave the earth. If a molecule exceeds this velocity, there is a chance for it likewise to be lost in space.

As we have seen, our earth was probably formed by the accumulation of solid particles floating in a hydrogen-and-helium gas mixture. If it had grown a few times more massive, it would have had a sufficiently strong gravitational field to retain an atmosphere of quite considerable amounts of these and other gases. This happened in the case of our larger sister planets Jupiter and Saturn. Their rocky cores, amounting to only about 2 per cent of their total masses, are covered with layers of frozen water, methane, and ammonia amounting to another 8 per cent. The remainder is nothing but highly compressed hydrogen and helium gas. The earth, being closer to the sun and smaller, had less gravitational field and was subjected to higher temperatures. These conditions were to play an important role in the steps that subsequently befell the newborn earth.

Because of rapid radiation of heat to space, the earth's surface temperature was probably never high enough to produce melting of the rocks that composed it. The temperature was nevertheless much higher than it is now. Forming as the earth is thought to have formed, it probably had a primitive atmosphere composed of hydrogen, helium, nitrogen, ammonia, and methane; also compounds of hydrogen and bromine, hydrogen and chlorine, hydrogen and fluorine, and hydrogen and sulfur. Certainly it would have been an unhealthy atmosphere for man. Because of the high temperatures prevailing, the molecules of these gases exceeded the escape velocity and were lost rapidly, in fact almost instantly as geological time goes. The earth was thus early orphaned, a barren sphere in the immensity of space.

Having lost its first blanket of gases, the simmering mass that was the earth of this period gradually lost heat also. While we do not know that eruptions occurred that may be classed as volcanoes, activity on a scale dwarfing by comparison present eruptive activity most likely prevailed. It is probable that the gases evolved during this period, being of similar terrigenic origin, were not unlike the gases given off from volcanoes today. The mean composition of gases from Halemaumau in Hawaii, for example, during recent years has been, by volume, 68 per cent water vapor, 13 per cent carbon dioxide, and 8 per cent nitrogen, with the remainder being mainly sulfurous fumes. There is no free oxygen given off now, and there probably was none then. During the first stages of this period, these gases must have been lost into space just as the initial gases had been. As the earth continued to cool, however, such losses diminished and then ceased almost entirely. The water vapor began to condense, deluging the earth and filling the oceans. Some of the carbon dioxide dissolved in the water, and some was taken up by carbonate rocks. The earth again obtained an atmosphere of water vapor, carbon dioxide, and nitrogen; and, having cooled considerably, it could retain it. It too was neither an atmosphere in which man could survive nor the atmosphere we have now. For man's survival, free oxygen has to be present. That oxygen was probably released by a photosynthesis reaction involving carbon dioxide and very elemental plant life.

Again we must consider the continued cooling of the earth. When the oceans formed they were quite hot, nearly boiling in fact. Slowly this oceanic cauldron cooled to a point at which life processes could begin. Just how life started has been the subject of speculation for centuries, and we cannot cover it here. Perhaps the first really significant information on the earliest stages of pre-life processes had been reported by Dr. Stanley L. Miller, who set up in a University of Chicago laboratory an atmosphere of the gases believed prevalent in the earth's primitive atmosphere and subjected it for periods of about one week to artificial lightning in the form of electric discharges. He then analyzed his atmosphere and detected numerous compounds, particularly amino acids, compounds found today in living organisms. Of course, finding that these acids can be produced artificially does not settle anything, for it is a long step from an organic molecule to the simplest bacterium that can reproduce itself. It is nevertheless a start. The early forms of life were probably very simple bacteria, perhaps like some we have today which do not require oxygen, for example, the purple sulfur bacteria. These organisms produce oxygen in a sulfur atmosphere. Or the first oxygen producers may have been the algae *Corycia*, fossil remains of which have been found nearly one and one-half billion years old. Still other organisms similar to these may have produced the first significant quantities of oxygen. This oxygen, in turn, prepared the way for green and more complex plants, which could produce great quantities of oxygen and thus support higher forms of life. As plant life developed, it bound up the carbon dioxide. The earth at last gained an atmosphere composed of the gases we find in it today.

It was probably a billion years ago that this basic atmosphere was first attained. Since that time volcanoes have continued to pour forth more water vapor, carbon dioxide, and nitrogen. From this stream, the water vapor ended in the oceans; the carbon dioxide, permitting greater quantities of ever more luxuriant plants to grow, released oxygen, the carbon going into deposits of coal and oil; while the nitrogen continued to accumulate. Thus today we have an atmosphere that is about 78 per cent nitrogen, 21 per cent oxygen, and the remainder water vapor and so-called rare gases. Change in the atmosphere has not stopped; it has merely slowed to a walk. The rare and inert gas argon is increasing as a result of the radioactive decay of one form of the element potassium, and now industrial activity is pouring forth a torrent of carbon dioxide and other compounds.

In summary, the origin of our planet's mantle of air is linked to the birth of our universe. It can be traced from the beginning of creation through the stage when all was gas and primeval darkness, through the development of stars in all their brilliance, to a seemingly sterile planet from the depths of which our present air emerged. In truth, if the story of this beginning had to be told in one sentence, it could not be more succinctly or eloquently expressed than when it was written, "And God said, Let there be light: and there was light."

3 the roof overhead

*Naught is seen in the vault on high
But the moon, and the stars, and the
cloudless sky.*

JOSEPH RODMAN DRAKE

A FEW decades hence excursions into the upper reaches of our earth's atmosphere will be but an afternoon's outing, an adventure nearly as commonplace as is a sight-seeing cruise on a glass-bottomed boat today. Impressive though it will be, as the earth drops away, to encompass an area of many states with one glance, the most striking feature of such a trip will be the radical change that takes place in the sky's appearance. Loosed at last from our home at the bottom of the air ocean, we will leave the clouds and other weather phenomena far below [Plate 1].* Gone will be the familiar blue; in its place will be only cosmic black. The stars will appear as needlesharp points of unsparkling light, while the sun will present a brilliant, well-defined disk with no glare.

To us, here considering the upper regions from our familiar en-

* See footnote on page 51.

vironment on earth, their most striking characteristic may well be their lack of substance. At a height of 9 miles atmospheric density is about one-eighth the sea level value. At higher elevations the density falls off quite rapidly, until at 60 miles it is only one one-millionth of that at sea level, or of the same magnitude as the so-called "vacuum" of ordinary light bulbs. The air contained in a cubic mile of space 120 miles above the earth weighs less than half a pound; in comparison the same volume at sea level weighs 5 million tons. At 185 miles the pressure is equivalent to that attained currently with the best laboratory vacuum pumps. Recalling that near sea level an average air molecule travels only a few millionths of an inch before colliding with another air molecule, it may be pointed out that at 9 miles this average distance of molecular travel has become 0.00004 of an inch, at 60 miles it is forty inches, while at an altitude of 185 miles it is about six miles.

To consider a region so tenuous may seem unnecessary and useless; that it could influence any aspect of our daily lives may appear impossible. Nevertheless the influence of the upper regions is great indeed and quite out of proportion to the density of matter involved. Far overhead, atmospheric gases meet and challenge invaders from the sun and outer space. But for them we would be unprotected from the intense short-wave-length radiations of the sun. Long-distance radio reception would be impossible. The auroral displays that illuminate the long winter nights in the polar regions would disappear, and we would be bombarded by meteors traveling at great speeds. Thus little imagination is required to regard the upper reaches of our atmosphere as a great protective canopy, a roof overhead.

Aside from this, upper-atmospheric phenomena are of extreme interest and importance scientifically because they occur on a scale and under conditions impossible to reproduce on earth. In the laboratory, experiments with rarefied gases must be carried out using confining vessels, the walls of which produce spurious effects, but in the upper atmosphere there are no walls and nature conducts experiments on a grandiose scale. Furthermore, unexpected relations, many of which are still unexplained, have been indicated between conditions far overhead and those near the earth, the weather for example. Finally and obviously, the high regions are of great practical importance to the development of high-flying aircraft, rockets, and missiles.

Various names have been assigned to particular regions of the upper atmosphere, even though there is no well-marked demarcation line separating them. The boundaries vary with the seasons, the latitude, and lower-level atmospheric conditions. In all systems of classification the atmosphere is considered to be composed of a succession of shells encompassing the earth. The most common system, and the one we shall use primarily, is based on temperature.

The first and lowest shell is called the troposphere and extends from sea level to a height of about seven miles. All points on the earth are within this region, although Mount Everest lifts its lofty peak nearly to the limit. The region from the troposphere to about 22 miles is called the stratosphere; that from the stratosphere to 50 miles is the mesosphere; the thermosphere extends to 250 miles; and the region farther beyond is the exosphere. The suffix "-pause" is employed to indicate the upper boundary of a shell. Thus the tropopause is the boundary between the troposphere and the stratosphere, the stratopause between the stratosphere and the mesosphere, and so on. Certain regions have also been given special names signifying their dominant characteristic. We have the ozonosphere as the region in which the gas ozone is predominant, the chemosphere as the region in which chemical reactions brought about by the sun's radiations are most important, and the ionosphere as that where radiations produce a witch's brew of metastable molecules and ions, atomic entities having electric charges.

Perhaps we can best explore these regions by taking a make-believe trip through them. Since we begin our journey at the bottom of the air ocean, our first zone is the troposphere. As we rise through it, the temperature decreases until a thermometer would indicate a level of about minus 65 degrees Fahrenheit as we enter the stratosphere. With only a gentle breeze blowing on the earth now left behind, we discover that wind speed has increased considerably. The pressure, meanwhile, has dropped to about one-quarter of its sea-level value. Thus the troposphere contains some three-quarters of all the mass of the atmosphere; in it the drama of our weather, outlined in subsequent chapters, is acted out.

During our passage through the stratosphere a warming of the air, amounting at most to a few degrees, is detected. At first wind velocity decreases, but as we approach a height of about twelve miles, increasing velocities are encountered which reach, perhaps, 150 miles an hour. In this shell also we first encounter appreciable quantities of the "Dr. Jekyll and Mr. Hyde" compound, ozone. To it we owe our existence, but we dare not breathe it, for ozone destroys a man's lungs. Formed from oxygen by a two-stage process of disassociation and recombination under strong short-wave-length radiations from the sun, ozone is quick-tempered and unruly. We do not entirely escape its wrath on earth. Traces of ozone filter down to the lowest levels of the atmosphere and attack with corrosion and rot. For example, ozone causes the deterioration of rubber products after a few years. Its quantity in the troposphere seems to be intimately related to weather processes, but just how is unknown. Where and when we make our imaginary ascent will determine to some extent the quantity of it we encounter. For reasons not yet explained completely, there seems to be more ozone in the stratosphere near the earth's poles than at the equator, and more in the spring of the year than in the fall and winter.

Although the quantities of ozone even in the upper atmosphere are relatively small, the amount is sufficient to absorb most of the sun's sunburn-producing rays and prevent their reaching earth. Thanks to ozone, then, we enjoy sun-bathing and outdoor summer sports. The stopping, or absorption as it is technically called, of a portion of the sun's energy is responsible for the increase in temperature observed in the stratosphere, and the existence of a zone having a relatively high temperature has great significance with regard to conditions on the earth. As we shall see subsequently, warm air at the surface of the earth tends to rise and be replaced by colder air. But since a parcel of air will continue to rise only as long as the air about it is cooler, the region of relatively warm air in the stratosphere in effect says to the air rising from the earth, "You can go this far and no farther." Much of the heat received from the sun is thus prevented from escaping into space. As we leave the stratosphere, we have passed through almost 99 per cent of the matter in the atmosphere.

In the next region, the mesosphere, temperature changes drastically. By the time we have reached a height of thirty miles, it has attained something like 170 degrees. From this point it decreases until, at the upper limit of the mesosphere, the mesopause, it has dropped to minus 28 degrees. Pressure has continued its decrease, although by this height it is so low that further reduction can hardly be detected. In the lower levels of the mesosphere ozone was prevalent, but it too has become inconsequential as we have progressed upward. If we peer carefully into the blackness that surrounds us, we may see a fiery object shoot past or terminate in our vicinity, for we are now in the region where meteors clash with the atmosphere.

In the thermosphere, as the name implies, we encounter one outstanding characteristic, an increase in gas temperature. Since we left the mesosphere the temperature of the air, such as remains, has increased steadily, reaching several thousand degrees, but it is temperature without commensurate heat. When we measure air temperatures on earth with a thermometer, we really obtain an indication of the energy being transmitted to the thermometer's glass bulb by a multitude of air molecules colliding with the bulb; the faster the molecules travel, the higher we call the temperature. Because there are so many billions of them crowded together, a molecule on earth barely gets going before it suffers a collision and loses its energy. Thus the average earth-bound air molecule never has a chance to build up high energy or temperature; but, as a result of the host of molecules comprising the air, large total energy, or heat, is involved. In the thermosphere, on the other hand, a gas molecule can accelerate for many miles unhampered by collisions.

It therefore attains high collision energy—enough to sever it into atoms, ions, and lesser molecular fragments, in fact—but the sparsity of molecules prevents any great accumulation of heat. The situation may be likened to two baseball teams, one composed of nine ordinary players and another of a single superb star player. It goes without question that the nine ordinary men are a far more effective unit than the one superlative man.

Since the great distances molecules travel in the thermosphere without encountering other molecules might lead to a misconception about all upper atmospheric regions as well as space itself, it should be said that molecular collisions are few and far between primarily because gas molecules are infinitesimally small and not because the distances between them are great. There are many thousands of gas particles, or fragments, in each cubic inch of the thermosphere, and probably several thousand in the same volume of deepest interstellar space. For comparison, one cubic inch of the air we breathe, it will be recalled from Chapter 1, contains 490 billion billion molecules, so even a few thousand entities is relatively very few, but it by no means represents a void.

If we were to leave the protection of our imaginary ship in the thermosphere, we would not be conscious of any ambient gas temperature, or of any gas at all for that matter. Unless shielded by the earth itself, we would be subjected to the sun's radiation on one side and to nearly total darkness on the other. Consequently one side of our body would boil while the other froze. If our trip has taken us near the North Pole, we may see at close range the aurora borealis; or near the South Pole, the aurora australis. We may also encounter terrific wind velocities but, again because of the extremely low air density, little force will be exerted upon us. Rocket experiments nevertheless have shown that currents can sweep westward at nearly 400 miles an hour some 50 miles above the earth and eastward at a similar speed a few miles higher, perhaps at an altitude of 65 miles.

Beyond the thermosphere lies the exosphere, encompassing the limit of our atmosphere. This is a region of extreme material sparsity, high gas-particle velocities, and consequently high gas-particle temperatures; within it, if latest indications are correct, there lies a zone composed almost entirely of dissociated hydrogen atoms, i.e., electrons and protons. Pressures are so low as to be meaningless. From this region gases sometimes escape the earth's gravitational pull to begin an eon of endless drifting. Beyond it there is only space interspersed with these molecules and molecular fragments, occasional rock and metal chunks left over from the earth's formation (Chapter 1) or originating from exploded stars and disintegrated comets, and, of course, at great distances other stellar bodies. Let us therefore terminate our make-believe journey and examine some of the consequences of what we have perceived.

Unlike the infinitesimally small gas molecules that sometimes defy the gravitational pull of the earth, chunks of matter readily succumb to the earth's attraction when they come near. Occasionally the earth runs through a cloud of stellar debris, and at such times there would be a bombardment of the earth's surface suggestive of an artillery barrage were it not for the atmosphere. These celestial vagabonds plow into the upper atmosphere as they rush on their way to the earth. Here they are heated to incandescence by impact with the air, and most of them are consumed.

Meteoric incandescence generally begins at a height of about seventy miles and ends more than forty miles from the earth. This, then, is the region of visibility for meteors, or shooting stars as they are commonly called. Visible meteors are, for the most part, less than the size of a pea, though they appear much larger because of their envelope of glowing gases. Most meteors are much smaller than a grain of sand and do not leave visible trails. The larger ones, however, are not always consumed during their flight through the upper atmosphere; about one in an estimated twenty million is too large to be burned completely, and its remnants collide with the earth. Several of these have struck and killed people in recorded times, and a few have dug vast craters. The true nature of meteors has been established only in relatively recent years. Thomas Jefferson, for example, when told New England college astronomers maintained that "shooting stars" were really chunks of matter from space, remarked, "I would rather believe that Yankee professors have lied than that rocks actually fall from heaven."

Meteors enter the atmosphere at speeds ranging between seven and forty miles per second. The quantity of material they add to the earth is calculated to be quite large, perhaps two thousand tons per day. Almost all of this matter reaches the earth's surface as a very fine dust or ash, and we are unaware of it. However, when you dust a piece of furniture it may occasionally be appropriate to ponder the fact that your effort is necessary partly because of matter newly arrived from space.

The ionized trail meteors leave in the region between sixty and seventy miles above the earth currently is giving to radio communication one of its most exciting developments. Very high-frequency radio signals bounced off meteor trails permit improved communications, particularly in the far north, where atmospheric irregularities often accompany the aurora. To make use of the system, antennas of two specially equipped radio stations, which may be as much as a thousand miles apart, must be aimed at the same point of the sky. When a meteor hits within the intersecting beams of both antennas and leaves a reflecting trail, a signal flashes out from the station designated to receive, electronically telling the other station to relay its message. This the latter does, also through electronics, in a "burst" of activity that lasts for only a second, the usable lifetime of a meteoric trail. But since several hundred satisfactory meteor trails are formed in the zone of antenna-beam intersection each hour, messages can be relayed without undue delay.

Not only is our upper atmosphere bombarded by stellar debris and subjected to intense radiations from the sun; into it flows a daily traffic of tiny corpuscles, really protons and electrons, from the sun, which "rain" upon the atmosphere and produce the spectacular auroras or the northern and southern lights, as they are sometimes called. These bits of the sun's substance are channeled toward the polar regions by the earth's magnetic field, thus accounting for auroras being most frequent near the poles. They are occasionally seen, however, from every point on the globe; records indicate that an auroral display is visible over the tropics about once every ten years. Auroral visibility begins some six hundred miles above the earth and ends at an altitude of about sixty miles.

The aurora is formed at its highest levels from a combination of the protons (hydrogen nuclei) of the corpuscular stream and electrons to form hydrogen atoms, a union that produces light. Later, light apparently comes from interactions involving beams of the electrons. The mechanism responsible for the aurora is thus much the same as that of a neon sign.

Being electrified, the streams of corpuscles from the sun disturb the earth's magnetic field high in the upper atmosphere. Our senses are completely oblivious to such changes, but homing pigeons and certain other migratory birds may possibly be conscious of them. Even though we do not directly experience any effect, we can certainly recognize a surge in corpuscle invasion. Great magnetic fluctuations that began on Easter Sunday, 1940, for example, stopped short-wave communication between the United States and Europe for many hours. Teletype and wire-photo networks were interrupted. Extra currents as great as sixty amperes were induced on high-voltage power lines, blowing major-circuit fuses and depriving large areas of electric current. There are also indications that important effects on our weather were produced by this magnetic storm, as well as by others. For example, geomagnetic records show that an unusually large corpuscular bombardment in August, 1953, was followed by a period of intense heat. Likewise the dust-bowl period of the early 1930's was a time of numerous magnetic fluctuations.

Speculations on the causes of the aurora and its variations many years ago suggested the presence of a permanent electrical-conducting region high in the atmosphere. The advent of radio, however, brought the problem to the fore. Radio waves, like light beams, travel in straight lines; and the fact that radio messages are successfully sent over long distances means simply that the carrying waves are reflected around the earth's curvature. Actually there are several reflecting layers in the atmosphere, or, perhaps more correctly, one continuous region with maxima and minima. For convenience, the entire conducting or reflecting zone is designated the ionosphere by scientists concerned primarily with its behavior, and letters with subscripts are assigned to particular layers or maxima. Thus today three principal regions are recognized: the E-region at about 60 miles, the F1-region at about 140 miles, and the F2-region at something like 220 miles.

The conducting regions are zones in which ions—atomic particles having an electric charge—are produced in relatively great numbers by ultraviolet light and electromagnetic radiation from the sun. Normally the E- and F1-regions exist only during the day; the F2-region rises during the day and falls at night, probably as a result of temperature changes. For reasons unknown, the E-region spasmodically forms in a patchy fashion at night. At certain seasons of the year the F1- and F2-regions tend to merge into a general F-region. In addition to this diurnal variation, solar activity, such as produces the eleven-year sunspot cycle, produces a pronounced change. In periods of greatest sunspot activity, the electron density of the F2 layer may be twice as great as during minimum activity. It may be that storms or heat and cold waves on the earth's surface also affect the regions.

Equally as intriguing as the aurora is a less well known upper atmosphere phenomenon called airglow. Every night our earth wears a weird yellow, red, and green halo, a filmy band of luminous clouds, suggestive of the Milky Way, that sweeps across the sky as if driven by hurricane winds of 150 miles an hour. Though it is rarely detected by human eyes, instruments reveal that the airglow's light is not inconsequential. If our eyes were attuned to its wave lengths we could see on the darkest nights about as we do in mid-twilight, the state of darkness in which we begin to need our car's headlights. It has been suggested that some animals make their way at night by being able to perceive the airglow.

While the aurora arises from a bombardment of the atmosphere by streams of charged particles emanating from the sun, airglow results from sun-excited chemical reactions in the upper atmosphere. Under the intense radiations of the sun, oxygen and sodium atoms somehow dissociate and then at night partially recombine in a manner such that light is emitted, green and red coming from oxygen and yellow from sodium. Each color emission varies in intensity with time, and all airglow radiations are irregular, exhibiting a "patchiness" throughout the sky that has so far defied complete explanation. The green glow tends to increase in brightness until about midnight but to decline thereafter. In contrast, the red radiation decreases during the evening hours and then increases slightly just before dawn. Also contributing to uncertainties about the airglow is its tendency to roam with the seasons. It seems to be more intense in summer and winter in the north and stronger in the autumn and spring in the south. Airglow appears to occur at about the same altitude as the aurora.

Still another intruder pours in upon the earth, subjecting the upper atmosphere to the full fury of his attack. This invader is cosmic radiation. Coming, packed with tremendous energy, in every direction from the depths of space and from the sun, cosmic rays crash into the atmosphere; but they do not penetrate, at least not directly. Somewhere high overhead—recent measurements indicate as much as twenty thousand miles out—every cosmic bullet collides with an air molecule. Fragments of the collision—electrons, ions, atoms, nuclear particles—shower down upon the earth, giving rise to numerous effects, some of which we shall develop more fully in other chapters. Here interest centers on upper-air nuclear reactions and their unstable, radioactive products.

One result of cosmic-ray bombardment is that ordinary nitrogen molecules are transmuted into a form of carbon, designated carbon 14, which in turn shows up in atmospheric carbon dioxide and eventually becomes a small part of all plant and animal tissue. As long as they live, plants and animals continue to ingest this special carbon along with the normal variety; but, of course, when they die all carbon intake ceases. Being radioactive, the carbon 14 decays and its quantity diminishes. In a little more than 5500 years, half of its amount in the remains of any plant or animal will have disappeared, and in another 5500 years only half of the remainder, or one-quarter of the original amount, will be present. Since this rate, reduction by half every 5500 years, continues indefinitely, radiocarbon from the atmosphere serves as a sort of built-in clock enabling accurate chronological dating to be made of events far in the past, an obvious boon to archeology.

Of course most plants and animals have decayed into dust long before archeologists become interested in them. Occasionally, however, the remains of an organism are fortuitously preserved, maybe as a fossil, a dwelling beam, or a bit of charcoal from a long-forgotten fire. From present-day measurements of the fraction of radiocarbon in living matter and sensitive instrument indications of the fraction of radiocarbon remaining in an ancient object of plant or animal origin, a simple calculation can show the time elapsing since the object stopped growing. Radiocarbon dating is thus the most useful single technique in the archeologist's repertoire, and it certainly is an odd development to have come from upper-air research.

Carbon is not, however, the only radioactive element produced in the upper air. Radiohydrogen, or tritium, like radiocarbon, is formed under cosmic ray bombardment and is likewise an excellent tracer for studying natural processes, even though its quantity in all the air never exceeds one ounce. Radiohydrogen, by working its way into a water-vapor molecule in the place of ordinary hydrogen, eventually reaches earth by way of precipitation. Thus it can tell us much regarding the time moisture remains in the air and the great movements of air and clouds about the face of the globe. A third natural radioactive atom, beryllium 7, is even more rare than tritium, but it too promises to be of value in resolving weather problems.

Weather is, as mentioned earlier, a low-level phenomenon; from great heights its moisture clouds appear as fluffy balls of cotton skimming along the ground [Plate 1]. Though clouds rarely grace the upper atmosphere, they are not completely unknown there.

Occasionally rare mother-of-pearl clouds are observed at about the fifteen- or sixteen-mile level. These are clouds of ice crystals, which show that small amounts of water vapor are present at this height. Very rarely luminous clouds having a shining bluish white color are seen at an elevation of perhaps fifty-five miles. These formations are called noctilucent clouds, and are thought to be due to dust particles from disintegrated meteors. They are best seen an hour or so after sunset when, because of their height, they are lighted by the sun though the sky is generally dark.

It is clear that strange and wonderful occurrences take place in the upper atmosphere and that this storehouse for nature's secrets is only beginning to be unlocked. Certainly conspicuous among the unexpected findings to date is the upper atmosphere's chemical composition, the presence of ozone being a prime example. But other constituents—nitrous oxide, methane, carbon monoxide, atomic oxygen, and neutral sodium atoms—have been found also. Nitrous oxide appears to be located largely in the troposphere; it is somewhat more abundant than ozone. Methane and carbon monoxide seem to be distributed about like the main body of the atmosphere; i.e., their quantities fall off quite rapidly with altitude; they must originate on the earth and diffuse upward. The total quantity of methane in all the atmosphere, if collected at the earth's surface, would amount to a layer only about one-third of an inch thick. Atomic oxygen is first detectable at about fifty-five miles, and beyond about seventy-eight miles all oxygen exists in this excited state. Nitrogen in a dissociated state is found at elevations beyond sixty-five miles. The really surprising constituent of the upper atmosphere is neutral sodium. How did a substance that is extremely reactive to traces of water get in the atmosphere, even the dry atmosphere of the high elevations? Does it come from space, from meteors and meteoric particles, or from the salt, sodium chloride, of the ocean?

If the importance attached to the rare constituents of the upper atmosphere, which, combined, comprise less than one one-millionth of the atmosphere, appears unusual, it can only be reiterated that there are many practical reasons for studying upper-atmospheric phenomena. In spite of its comparative lack of substance, the region is vital in the scheme of things on the earth. It harbors mysteries to which man will be seeking answers for many, many years. Investigations of the region, now being probed with man-made satellites, will surely intensify in the years to come, and its importance will mushroom as the conquest of space itself is pressed. We will return to this subject in the final chapter.

4 a restless sea

The wind goeth toward the south,
and turneth about unto the north;
it whirleth about continually,
and the wind returneth again
according to his circuits.

ECCLESIASTES I, 6

AT FEW places, and then at rare intervals, is movement of the air undetectable. In some areas of the world the winds almost always blow south, in others predominantly north, in still others east or west. They may blow straight up or straight down, and they are wont to change direction at a moment's notice. Perpetual air movement is inevitable and necessary in the scheme of nature.

Between the equator and latitudes 30 to 35 degrees north or south, the earth receives a surplus of solar energy, while poleward there is a net deficit, the loss of heat by radiation exceeding that gained from the sun. The air's circulation is the means whereby partial correction of this unbalanced condition is accomplished. Otherwise, the temperature of the middle and high latitudes would decrease steadily and that of the low latitudes would increase until a new balance between heat input and heat loss was reached in each zone. The resulting equilibrium temperatures would make the polar areas very much colder than they are now and the equatorial areas unbearably hot. Thus the winds that ever sweep around the earth may be considered a gigantic thermodynamic engine for distributing heat, an engine that derives its energy from the sun. The earth's rotation is the flywheel that directs the course of the winds.

The wind is saddled with a Herculean task, and tremendous quantities of energy ride upon its performance. The amount required just to keep the air moving is itself enormous; we have several million billion tons of air, it will be remembered. Should all circulation cease, energy equivalent to some seven million atomic bombs, or the power all United States electric generating stations could produce in a hundred years, would be required to start normal circulation again. But this is only the energy of motion; that transported about the earth by the air in the form of heat is an astronomical figure, for, as pointed out previously, on the average every one-and-one-half-square-mile area of the earth's surface receives energy from the sun equivalent to one Hiroshima-type atom bomb each day.

As in most natural phenomena, over-all patterns can be found in the air currents, upon which are superimposed intricate smaller schemes of behavior. Those best understood and of most direct consequence to us occur wholly within the troposphere, that shallow bottom layer of the atmosphere which, on the scale of an ordinary classroom globe, corresponds to little more than the thickness of a good coat of paint. To see how the general circulation of air about the earth originates, let us consider first two simple illustrations. With these we can establish the underlying principles of air movement about the earth.

When we blow cigarette smoke toward a lighted electric lamp, we see the smoke borne upward by the stream of heated air rising from the lamp. Warm air is lighter than cold air because its molecules are more energetic; they collide more often and rebound with more force. By so doing, they produce more free space about themselves, in much the same fashion that an ill-tempered person alienates and drives away his associates. Warm air thus tends to rise and to be replaced by cooler, denser air. The cool air as it comes near warm objects is itself heated. It thus rises and is replaced by cooler air, and so on.

As the second illustration, let us consider for a moment the somewhat improbable situation of fleas sitting on a rotating record-player turntable. To us, observing from a distance, a flea perched near the center would appear to be moving in a lazy little circle, while a flea sitting near the rim of the turntable would be traveling at a much faster rate. If our center flea attempted to jump to the position of his outer compatriot, he would surely miss his objective, for while the first flea was in flight, the outer flea would have moved some distance from his initial position.

Just as with the record-player turntable, there are great differences in the velocities with which parts of the earth move. Except by the rising and setting of the sun, we are not even conscious of the earth's rotation, but an Eskimo moves only a few hundred miles during one rotation of the earth, while a savage at the equator is moving thousands of miles. If an Eskimo were to travel toward the equator, it would be necessary for him to gain a bit of the earth's rotational velocity with each step he took. To be sure, the velocity gained with each step would be quite small and would be imperceptible to him, but it must be gained nonetheless. Moving masses of air, not being bound securely to the earth like our Eskimo, tend to undergo a change in direction when they shift from one latitude to another instead of taking on the new rotational velocity of the earth below. Fortunately, the air is not completely free of the earth as the jumping flea was free of the turntable. Surface irregularities, mountains, trees, buildings, exert a retarding effect that slows moving air masses. Since the earth at the equator rotates with a velocity of roughly one thousand miles an hour, winds of many hundreds of miles per hour could develop if it were not for this friction with objects on earth.

In accordance with our first principle, the rising of warm air, a general upward flow exists above the tepid water and steaming jungles of the equatorial regions. As this warm air attains stratospheric heights, it is cooled, but it is prevented from rising indefinitely by the zone of relatively warmer air, which, from Chapter 3, we saw existed at somewhat higher levels. The air is also prevented from falling back by other warm air coming up. The only thing left for it to do is to move either northward or southward, and, as we might expect, a general movement poleward is found at the higher equatorial elevation. To replace this air, cooler air must flow in from polar directions along the surface of the earth to feed the rising fountain of warmed air. Prevailing surface winds in the equatorial region are thus toward the central belt of the earth.

The earth's rotation, however, conforming to our second principle, prevents both the high- and low-level movements from being a direct poleward-to-equatorial flow. The air moving toward the poles at the higher levels has equatorial velocity when it starts its journey. It is like the flea on the rim of the turntable. As it progresses either northward or southward, it finds itself over parts of the earth's surface having lesser and lesser velocities. The air thus tends to outrun the land beneath it and appears to be moving in an ever more easterly direction. By the time latitudes 30 degrees north or south are reached, cooling and friction have taken their toll and the air settles back to the earth's surface. As a consequence this latitude is one of unusual calm, the horse latitudes—so named, one story holds, because sailing ships of former days, becalmed for long periods, found it necessary to jettison livestock, mostly horses, due to shortages of food and water.

Conversely, air moving at low levels toward the equator from the 30-degree latitudes passes over land or ocean having ever increasing velocities. It suffers the opposite directional change and approaches equatorial latitudes moving westward, or, as we would say, as an east wind. These low-level prevailing east winds have become known as the trade winds, because, again in the days of sailing vessels, they were the steadiest and most dependable of all the general air circulation about the earth. They sped many a sleek clipper ship with its cargo of tea, passengers, and mail around the world a century ago. When at last the trade winds reach the central regions, they become warmed and begin their rise to stratospheric levels to complete the cycle. The lateral motion that we think of as wind turns into vertical motion, and the air rises as if it were smoke from a great atmospheric chimney. The result is another zone of near-ground-level windlessness around the earth's middle, the doldrums, the bane of merchantman captains in the days before powered ships.

The polar regions present a characteristic, although less reliable, circulation pattern also. Cold air descends on the poles and spills down the earth in the general direction of the equator. But by the time this polar air reaches latitudes in the region of 60 degrees north or south, the earth's rotation has altered its apparent direction of motion to such an extent that the flow is almost entirely toward the west; in other words, to persons on the ground the wind seems to be blowing from the east. Hence the origin of the prevailing polar easterlies. Although the use of the term "warmed" is open to question, this polar air is warmed relatively at this latitude, and it begins to rise to higher elevations. Once elevated, the air may return by a high-level route to the pole to begin its journey again, or it may become entangled in the turbulence that characterizes the air between equatorial and polar regions.

These areas between encompass the temperate zones wherein live three-quarters of the earth's population. These zones are temperate only in the sense that air flooding back and forth from the poles and the equator can make a place, New York for instance, seem to be one day on the outskirts of the tropics and the next day part of the arctic. The changing fortunes of the atmospheric skirmishing between warm and cold air masses all but obliterate any over-all pattern of circulation in the middle region. In general, however, summer surface winds blow from the southwest (in the Northern Hemisphere) under the predominant influence of the great atmospheric circuit rising above the equator, and winter winds from the northwest due to the slowly sinking air of the North Pole. The prevailing westerly winds of the central belt thus move in opposition to the polar easterlies and the equatorial trade winds. If somewhere about this planet there were not counteracting westerly winds, the drag, or braking effect, of the polar and equatorial air zones would have slowed the earth's rotation greatly if not stopped it altogether during the long history of our planet.

Into this basic circulation pattern many factors weave their imprints, so that the actual direction of the winds at any time can be almost anything. Our earth does not spin with its axis rigidly aligned with respect to the sun; the earth's motion is more like that of a wobbling top. This tilting causes the seasons and the apparent march of the midday sun back and forth across the equator. It also produces periodic unbalances in the atmosphere, causing the circulation system in either hemisphere to be ever expanding or contracting.

The doldrums and the trade winds shift easily with the sun's progress because the tropics, being directly exposed to the sun's rays, respond quickly and adjust rapidly to the influx of radiant energy. Polar regions on the other hand, receiving most of their heat indirectly, adjust slowly. Between the two, the temperate zones must bear the brunt of the inevitable altercation. Here the thrusts of the warm, rapidly adjusting equatorial air are met by the stubbornly resisting polar air. The adjustment must be most rapid in March and September, for these are the times when, like a pendulum at its central position, the sun is marching fastest. Then we notice the most rapid lengthening or shortening of the days. During these periods storms are most likely to sweep across the middle latitudes. In June and December the sun reaches the crest of its apparent march; it is like a pendulum at the extremity of its swing, it stands for a moment motionless, poised to make its sweep in the opposite direction. These are periods of little adjustment and comparative meteorological stability on the surface.

The general circulation is forced also to adjust to geographic differences, to react locally. Air is lifted over lofty mountain ranges, heated over deserts, cooled over expanses of ice or snow, and warmed or chilled by great oceans. Over the Pacific and Atlantic oceans great horizontal circulations develop. Near the horse latitudes cool air from the base of the stratosphere sinks onto the central areas of these oceans. As it spreads out laterally, it warms and the earth's rotation imparts to it a circular motion. Enormous wheels of revolving air are thus developed over each ocean, one each over the North Atlantic and the North Pacific, with similar circulations over the South Atlantic and South Pacific. The pair in each hemisphere move as if geared together, those of the Northern Hemisphere turning clockwise and their opposite numbers in the Southern Hemisphere turning counterclockwise. As air is fed into their centers, their winds sweep in wider and wider circles above the oceans. From the edges, occasional masses of air are thrown out like water from a revolving lawn sprinkler. Such air coming up from the direction of the Caribbean brings warm weather to the eastern United States and cool air from the North Atlantic to the British Isles. Over the Pacific, cool air from its northern area may sweep our western states while warm air from the southern seas assails Japan.

Over the continents the air's circulation is greatly modified by mountain chains. In ages past, when the earth was younger and her face unwrinkled, winds could sweep nearly unobstructed from the equator to the poles. The climate of the polar areas must have been much more salubrious then; indeed it seems that the whole earth had a more uniform climate at this stage. The most extreme example of the effect of mountains today is found over Asia. Eastward from Turkey mountains run through Persia into Afghanistan. From there one branch extends above Mongolia to the Bering Sea, while another runs across the top of India as the Himalayas, the highest mountains of the world. These mountains form the southern and eastern boundaries of the largest land mass on earth, and are a barrier that prevents ready interchange of air masses. In the spring, as the sun begins to send her warm rays upon western China, the land and the air above it become heated. The heated air begins rising, and the sun sends down more and more energy as spring turns into summer. Heat accumulation continues until the atmospheric suction pulls air lying over India, southeastern Asia, and the surrounding oceans and seas as far away as Ceylon and the Philippines up the slopes of the encircling mountains. The result is the monsoon, the wind that blows inland from the sea in late summer bringing heavy rains. In the winter, the same mountains act as a barrier to the cold, heavy air moving down from Siberia. Eventually, when enough cold has accumulated, the air spills over the mountain chain like flood waters over a dam, inundating large areas of Asia with chilled and frosty air. On our own continent, principal mountain chains run north and south. Thus there is little to obstruct the interchange of cold and hot air between northern Canada and the Gulf of Mexico.

On a smaller scale, land and sea breezes, or land and lake breezes, are produced by an analogous reversal of temperatures between day and night along the shores, the land warming by day more than the water and cooling also more at night. The breeze, blowing into the warmer area, moves from the water toward the land during the day and in the opposite direction after darkness. Such winds are most pronounced in the tropics and best developed where sea and mountains meet. East Indian fishermen, for example, put out with the land breeze in the morning and return home in the evening with the sea breeze. Other examples of diurnally reversed winds are mountain and valley breezes. By night, relatively cold, heavy air pours down the mountain slopes. During the day the air warms and expands, and, being confined by the mountains, flows up the slopes as a valley breeze. Of course the proximity and location of lakes, mountains, mountain passes, and the like can cause an almost limitless variety of wind conditions.

A violent wind with gusts up to two hundred miles per hour that blows outward from the Adelie coast of Antarctica for long periods in the winter is the result of such a peculiar topographical feature. A great sloping trough two to three hundred miles wide, formed by the Queen Maud Range of mountains on one side and ice deposits on the other, leads inland from the coast to, or nearly to, the South Pole. Heavy, extremely cold air of the high Antarctic interior thus is provided with a flume down which it can spill, gain momentum like water through the spillway of a dam, and emerge over the sea as a howling gale. A jumbled pattern of upward and downward thermal currents often prevails over continental lands, particularly if the character of the terrain varies as when wooded lots alternate with cultivated or barren plots. For evidence we need only watch for a while the graceful circles soaring birds describe in the sky. This behavior on the part of birds is neither the result of gregariousness, an abhorrence of straight lines, nor a manifestation of an ability to defy the laws of nature, as an ornithologist once described it. It is simply the birds' way of staying in localized columns of warm air that spurt up from the most heated land below. Men too have learned to ride the thermal currents in light, motorless, soaring planes. By so doing they have also discovered that a current, one moment rising, can dissolve almost as rapidly as a bubble breaking at a liquid surface and become a downward air movement. Thermal currents are at times large and smooth; often, of course, on a summer afternoon they are likely to be capped with cumulus clouds, the familiar thunderheads.

On more than one occasion pilots have bailed out of crippled planes, only to be carried up instead of down by strong updrafts. On at least one occasion the pilot was carried to such an altitude that his hands and feet froze. On still another a pilot was tossed about in complete darkness for thirty minutes after bailing out before the first signs of earth were sighted. He was unable to say how high or far he was carried, but about the time he was certain. His watch had a glowing dial, and as he said, "I had nothing to do but look at it."

There are also winds, high winds, in the upper atmosphere, which appear to be as variable and complex as the systems of the lower levels. Our information about them now is fragmentary, but studies of meteor trail bending, noctilucent cloud movement, balloon drift, sound propagation, and the like indicate that winds in the northern hemisphere between twenty and fifty miles up are mostly from the east or northeast in summer and from the west or northwest in winter. Above fifty miles there are indications of predominantly west winds all year round, but this is far from a certainty.

Near the tropopause is found a very active wind system that produced one of the strangest tales to come from World War II. Our first truly strategic aircraft, the famous B-29, was designed to fly at altitudes just short of the stratosphere, it being anticipated that, at this altitude, interception would be difficult and antiaircraft fire ineffectual. Indeed, except for the inevitable difficulties of a new plane and a new mission, the first bombing runs with these planes over Japan were much like training flights. Soon, however, flights were forced back short of their targets with dwindling reserves of fuel, driven far off course, or even forced to ditch in the ocean by strange wind phenomena. Navigators reported that, despite air speed indications of three hundred miles per hour, their planes sometimes stood still over the ground, and, when they turned after bombs were dropped, their ground speed was about twice the air speed indicated by their instruments. Under the urgency of military necessity it was soon established that high-level, generally eastward-moving currents exist, some parts of which move faster than any gale has ever moved on the surface. This upper-level air current was appropriately named the jet stream [Plate 2].

While our military operations over Japan are generally credited with discovery of the jet stream, the existence of high-level currents was not unknown prior to that time. As early as 1933, German scientists detected a relatively narrow, high-speed air-stream associated with the upper westerlies. The Japanese too had discovered it, and during 1944 and 1945 attempted fire-bombing the United States with balloon bombs hitching rides across the Pacific at altitudes of six to eight miles. They succeeded in sending fire-bombs as far inland as Montana, but the operation was unsuccessful largely because of the erratic movement of these winds.

The jet stream, it is now established, is an ever present component of the general atmospheric circulation; it is not an occasional freak condition. Scientists have not yet been able to probe it as thoroughly as they hope to do, but its outstanding features are known. The jet stream is a relatively narrow river of air—only up to three hundred miles wide—on either side of which are strips of calmer air. It is not one continuous stream around the world but is more of a series of gusts, albeit rather large ones. Anywhere from just north of the equator nearly to the pole and between ten and forty thousand feet, these narrow filaments of air may run at high speeds for thousands of miles.

Highest velocities are usually encountered at about forty thousand feet, just at the base of the stratosphere. In the wintertime greatest jet-stream velocities are above the region between 25 and 30 degrees north latitude, the horse latitudes, zones of unusual calm on the surface. During this period also, greatest velocities are found just off the Asiatic coast not far from where our B-29 crews first encountered winds of unbelievable velocities, over the southeastern United States, and between North Africa and the Indian Ocean. In the winter of 1954 a balloon being tracked by radar four miles aloft over Philadelphia was carried along at 392 miles per hour by the jet stream, although at the time a mere 12-mile-an-hour breeze was blowing on the ground. The jet stream shifts in summer to about 45 degrees north latitude, and its peak velocity falls to less than half its wintertime value. We do not have enough information at present to chart the corresponding current of the Southern Hemisphere, but such data as are available, principally over Australia and New Zealand, indicate a similar pattern of behavior.

There is not yet complete agreement on the cause of the jet stream, or more accurately the jet streams. It is almost certain, however, that they are the result of pressures between masses of cold polar air pushing south and warm tropical air pushing north. It may be that solar energy absorbed by a zone in the general vicinity contributes to the streams' velocities. That highest velocities are found over regions where warm ocean currents flow near colder land masses is undoubtedly significant, for the writhing, undulating course that the streams take accomplishes much heat interchange between equatorial and polar zones. Jet streams fundamentally affect the weather of much of the world.

Convolutions of the jet streams are responsible, for example, for our "topsy-turvy" weather, that occasional condition when portions of the southern United States are colder than Alaska. This occurs after a jet stream has lashed about so furiously that gigantic pools of arctic and tropical air have been cut off from the main stream as it gets back on its more normal course. The vast quantities of air that are transmitted across continents by jet streams sometimes bring sustained hot or cold spells. When a jet-stream pattern persists for weeks at a time, as it sometimes does, droughts or floods may result. In a general way the jet-stream seems to be a guiding mechanism for storms as well as fair weather across the middle latitudes. Tornadoes frequently appear to be born underneath a jet stream. The jet stream is thought to deflect, or even to direct, the paths of hurricanes. A shift in the path of the jet stream is held responsible for the increased frequency of these storms along the upper eastern and New England coasts and the corresponding decrease along the Florida coasts of the past few years. A Japanese typhoon is believed to have been thrown way off its course in 1953 by a shift in the undulating path of the jet stream, causing nearly a thousand persons on an unwarned ferryboat to drown.

Putting jet streams to use by having planes hitch rides on their rapid currents has not measured up to first expectations, again largely because of their erratic paths. This is particularly true over the Atlantic, where jet streams rarely can be counted on for a free ride. Over the Pacific, however, jet streams run more smoothly and more nearly on schedule. There, when a pilot locates a stream, he can slip his plane into it with the passengers noticing but a slight bump, and cut hours off his flying time. The results are occasionally spectacular. Not so long ago an Air Force transport plane, taking advantage of a jet stream, flew nonstop from Tokyo to Honolulu in nine hours and nine minutes, seven hours under the regular one-stop flying time.

Thus winds arise when there is a temperature difference between two parts of the earth's surface and hence a corresponding difference in the overlying air. As long as our earth maintains her canopy of air and rotates in her wobbly fashion around an incandescent sun with nearly heatless space at her back, and as long as her face is wrinkled yet only partially exposed above the water oceans, there will be contrasting temperatures, both locally and on a large scale. The winds seem destined to blow eternally.

5 the heavens in tumult

An horrid stillness first invades the ear,
And in that silence we the tempest fear.

JOHN DRYDEN

STORMS, LIKE eddies and whirlpools in the flood waters of a great river, all too frequently develop in the air currents sweeping about the earth. Arising from a variety of conditions, some of them may threaten for weeks, while others burn themselves out in a frenzy of activity during a summer afternoon. One storm may disrupt the activities of a continent, another be confined to an area measured in acres. They bring both life-giving rain and destruction, and in one form or another storms frequent nearly every section of the globe.

We call them by many names—thunderstorms, hailstorms, rainstorms, snowstorms, dust storms, hurricanes, cyclones, tornadoes, and blizzards. Though each has its distinguishing feature, all have one thing in common—wind. A thunderstorm, as its name suggests, displays much lightning and thunder. A dust storm is one characterized by great quantities of flying dust. But the dust is incidental to the winds that carry it along; and the lightning and thunder have no influence, except possibly in the case of a tornado, on the beginning, the course, or the end of the storm of which they are notable features. The disturbance develops from shifting air masses; precipitation, as explained later, contributes fuel; and then the attendant phenomena are acquired which suggest the name.

Strictly, storms exist only when a certain wind velocity is reached. In 1805 British Admiral Sir Francis Beaufort, in order to give mariners a guide in ship and rigging handling, devised a scale in which storm winds were those that destroyed sails and were likely to damage vessels in other ways. Numerical wind speeds were incorporated in the original scale in 1906, and the latter is almost universally recognized today. On the Beaufort Scale, as it is still called, storm winds begin at sixty-four miles per hour. Hurricane and tornadic winds greatly exceed this velocity; thunderstorm winds attain it sometimes. We shall confine the following, therefore, to phenomena that are storms in the true sense of the word.

The most destructive of all atmospheric disturbances on earth with which men must contend is the hurricane. It does not pack the concentrated fury of a tornado, nor does it cover at any one time nearly as large an area as some other disturbances—a blizzard, for example. What it lacks in either category, however, it more than makes up in combined violence and sweep. During its lifetime—sometimes several weeks—a hurricane may spread destruction over more than a half-million square miles. Its winds often reach 150 miles per hour, and it is likely to generate a score of tornadoes on its outskirts. When mature, a hurricane expends energy at the fantastic rate of 500 trillion horsepower, or several million times that of all the electric-power stations in the United States. A single hurricane can dissipate more energy than that contained in thirty thousand atomic bombs.

In the China Sea area, a hurricane may be called a typhoon (from *ty fung,* meaning "great wind") or a baguio; in Australia, the same type of storm is called a willy-willy; in India, it is a Bengal cyclone. Except that typhoons, growing over the vast expanse of the western Pacific, are larger, all represent the same phenomenon. Columbus was the first European to experience one of these tropical disturbances, and he probably applied either the Indian word *huracan,* meaning "evil spirit," or *Hunraken,* after the Indian god of stormy weather, to the phenomenon, giving us our present terminology. History records that Columbus greatly feared these tropical storms. In 1494 he hid his ships behind a Caribbean island to escape one, only to have three of his vessels destroyed by another the following year. The experience led him to declare, "Nothing but the service of God and the extension of the monarchy would induce me to expose myself to such dangers."

A hurricane piles up great waves in the sea and drenches land areas with unimaginable deluges of water. As recently as the fall of 1955, four hundred persons were killed, mostly by drowning, in the east and northeast sections of the United States by one hurricane in one twenty-four-hour period. Nearly two billion dollars' worth of property damage was also sustained. Again in 1957 over five hundred lives were lost during a single hurricane that hit the Louisiana coastal area. In 1935 a hurricane-generated wave killed more than four hundred persons in the Florida Keys; more than six thousand were drowned by a similar wave at Galveston in 1900; while in India in 1876 an inundation produced by a hurricane caused more than one hundred thousand to perish. Fat merchantmen, as well as sleek battleships, are not immune to the wildly shrieking winds. In December, 1944, America's Third Fleet, lacking sufficient information to track the course of a Pacific typhoon, ran directly into it. Three ships were sunk, twenty-one were damaged, 146 planes were blown overboard, and 763 men were lost.

Hurricanes form most often in the late summer and early autumn over the tepid waters of the doldrums, that equatorial belt of calm between the trade winds. Spawned about 10 degrees north or south of the equator, they first move leisurely westward. Then, in the Northern Hemisphere, they curve upward along the rim of the Pacific or Atlantic Ocean to strike at the Philippines, the China coast, and Japan, or along the east coast of the United States. In the Southern Hemisphere, they descend on Australia and the east coast of Africa. The South Atlantic region is free of such storms, apparently because its waters are not warm enough to favor their development. Once formed, hurricanes press relentlessly on until the moist air on which they feed is cut off by a continent or quenched by cold winds from the poles.

To anyone who can read the signs, a hurricane signals its approach days in advance. A slow rise in temperature, a steady drop in barometric pressure, and a reduction in the frequency of sea swells are the first signs. Far out at sea, the winds of the hurricane whip up giant waves, which, traveling outward at perhaps thirty miles per hour, carry the warning of impending danger. Normally, under the influence of the trade winds, swell frequency is about eight per minute; it changes to four or five as a hurricane approaches, and the waves increase in magnitude. If the waves persist in coming from one direction, the storm is approaching head on, but if the direction shifts, the center is passing to one side.

When the storm is about five hundred miles off, the first atmospheric signs appear. These are usually colorful streamers of high clouds that seem to radiate from a single point in the sky. As the cloud cover thickens, a halo may appear about the sun or moon. Soon low, dense clouds go scudding across the sky in a different direction from the higher ones. The final act in the cloud panorama is the approach of a heavy black cloud wall, called the bar cloud. Reaching up two to five miles, it extends as far as the eye can see. When it closes down, all doubt that a hurricane is approaching disappears. Violent, intermittent squalls begin. Lashing rain and howling gales soon follow, building up to a crescendo as the hurricane nears.

Warmth, moisture, and a flat surface permitting easy inflow of air at low levels are necessary for hurricane generation. As the sun beats down on a calm expanse of ocean, enormous volumes of air are heated and saturated with water vapor. The warmed air rises gently, and other air comes in from the sides to replace it; the motion is moderate, but it is on a vast scale. Just as the earth's rotation imparts a spiral motion to water going down a drain, a counterclockwise spin (in the Northern Hemisphere) is developed by the air moving in. The heated air spirals to higher and higher levels.

With increased elevation comes a reduction in pressure; pressure reduction produces expansion; expansion causes cooling; and cooling causes precipitation. Finally, precipitation releases the latent heat carried by the moist air, and the fuel that feeds the hurricane is ignited. The movement that was gentle at first becomes a breeze; the breeze becomes a gale; and soon a full-fledged hurricane may be spawned. But if the babe is not to die at birth, it must regurgitate at higher levels the vast quantities of air being fed it by the rising currents—air which, in a going hurricane, may exceed a million pounds per second. How this high-level outpouring is accomplished is not completely understood. It was entirely a mystery until daring men during World War II began testing the hurricane's temperature and pulse during airplane flights directly into the maelstrom. Even now much is inadequately explained, but we are no longer completely in the dark.

Above an altitude of some thirty thousand feet the uniform and reliable trade winds of the tropics disappear, and in their place is found an atmosphere that is both variable and turbulent. Here eddies, great circular movements of air, travel both clockwise and counterclockwise. When a clockwise eddy at the higher level teams up with a low-level, counterclockwise, incipient hurricane, the result is a pulsing, throbbing thing that perpetuates itself as long as warm, moist air is available for it to feed upon; for humid air can then be taken from the surfaces, the moisture and energy wrung from it, and the air discarded at high levels. The upward flow of air produces the visible streamers of clouds radiating out at high levels. The low-level inflow of air accounts for clouds scudding along the earth's surface into the hurricane.

A full-grown hurricane is thus a great doughnut of rapidly spiraling air and cloud between seventy-five and five hundred miles in diameter,* reaching skyward for perhaps ten miles [Plate 2]. The center, called the eye, is a zone of remarkable calm, which varies between five and fifty miles in diameter. Except for clouds near the surface, the eye is generally clear. From the hurricane's outer limits wind velocities increase inward, until just outside the eye they attain high speeds, the highest recorded being a velocity of 186 miles per hour reached at the Mount Washington weather observatory during a New England storm of 1938.

The hurricane's anatomy has been vividly presented by observers flying into them. One of the best descriptions is of the third-largest hurricane on record, a 1951 Pacific typhoon. Two hundred miles from this storm's center winds reached seventy-four miles an hour; in another fifty miles, they increased to one hundred miles an hour. Thereafter clouds completely engulfed the plane, and bursts of torrential rain and turbulent air hammered at it. Instead of flying, the plane seemed to float in solid sheets of water and to behave like a runaway elevator. Then suddenly the turbulence slackened, and the plane broke into dazzling sunlight with bright blue sky overhead. The eye of the hurricane was attained.

As the plane circled in the eye, an awesome display could be seen. The eye was a clear space some forty miles in diameter. Surrounding this clearing was a wall of clouds, which on one side rose vertically and on the other was banked like the seats of an immense football stadium [Plate 2]. The upper rim of the vortex

* The giant swirl of an even larger hurricane is seen from one hundred miles above the earth in the upper illustration of Plate 1. Centered near Del Rio, Texas, this cloud system is about one thousand miles in diameter. Another meteorological phenomenon shown is an advancing cold front, visible as a thin haze, which begins near the left-hand corner of the picture and runs very nearly parallel to the curvature of the earth. The photograph was put together using 310 frames of motion picture film exposed from an Aerobee rocket on October 5, 1954. Not until the composing job had been completed was it suspected that these interesting cloud formations had been captured.

rounded off smoothly at about 35,000 feet, revealing the background of blue sky. A dome of clouds rose a mile and a half above ocean level in the center. Through occasional breaks in these clouds, glimpses could be had of the ocean surface. Around the rim of the vortex, unimaginably violent, churning water was visible.

Sailors surviving to break into and then out of the eye of a hurricane also tell of the almost sudden easing of the winds as the eye is attained. The shroudlike mist and driving rain that only minutes before covered the sea all but disappears. Flocks of birds and swarms of insects, wearied by days of imprisonment by the circling winds without a resting place, descend on the ship. Sometimes the sun breaks through for brief moments; at other times, through a gray lightness, the encircling cloud wall can be seen. One has the feeling that he is looking up from the bottom of a great well.

The eye of a hurricane is its most unbelievable feature. To the unwary it can bring disaster, as it did to Miami on September 18, 1926. When the winds that had buffeted that city in the early morning hours ceased and a beautiful sunrise appeared, many people started on their daily routines, some leaving for their jobs, others repairing the damage already wrought, and still others swimming in the great surf. Within an hour, an opposite gale arose as the other part of the hurricane swept over the city. Hundreds were caught and drowned by the raging waters.

Although the spiraling winds of a hurricane reach high velocities, the lateral movement averages only about twelve miles per hour. Sometimes hurricanes almost stop in their sweep across the earth, and at other times, particularly if in the region of the prevailing westerlies, they may race forward at speeds up to sixty miles an hour. When a hurricane passes over land a sudden change in course usually occurs. Its behavior in this event is much like a child's spinning top, which, when it bumps into an object, ricochets off in a new direction.

Two hurricanes seldom show a tendency to merge. If two

develop in the same general area they attract each other, and a peculiar dance routine follows. They are first drawn together because each is sucking great volumes of air from the region between. Their intensity is accordingly diminished by the sharing. As the hurricanes draw near, however, their spinning causes each to circle the other like boxers sparring for advantage. But they never complete a full turn. After a brief inspection, they separate and move off in diverging paths, and as they pull apart, each increases its strength once more. Bermuda was spared by such a meeting of two hurricanes in September, 1951. As a devastating hurricane with winds up to 160 miles per hour bore down, another hurricane, some 450 miles farther out in the Atlantic, came into the picture. After waltzing about, both hurricanes raced off into the open Atlantic to die unmourned.

In general, hurricanes seem to be steered by the jet stream, that meandering, high-velocity river of air in the upper atmosphere. Most often during the past century, Atlantic hurricanes upon leaving the Caribbean have traveled from the southwest to the northeast, a course that has carried them roaring by Cape Hatteras, North Carolina, out into the open Atlantic. For the past two decades the most probable path has gradually shifted, until at the present it lies nearly north and south. The current path makes hurricanes much more likely to strike inland along the Atlantic seaboard or to head directly for New England. Why the path should have shifted and when the trend will be reversed is a subject about which there has been considerable speculation.

Some meteorologists think sunspot activity and its influence on the general atmospheric circulation most likely cause shifts in the courses of hurricanes. During periods of low sunspot activity, hurricanes tend to remain embedded in the easterly winds where they were born and to sweep across Florida and the southeastern states. With a rise in sunspot activity, however, prevailing winds undulate to the right and left of their previous paths. Westerly winds dip deep into Texas and the Gulf area, while easterly ones seem most inclined to move on a more northerly course. Northbound hurricanes then may be picked up by the westerlies and carried into the New England area.

If this systematic pattern is true we can expect 1957, which witnessed the peak of a forty-five-year period of increasing sunspot activity, to have been the turning point of hurricane assaults on New England. The present decade (1950-1959) will most likely mark the peak of hurricane frequency in the western Atlantic as contrasted with the Gulf area. During the 1960-1969 decade hurricane incidence along the Atlantic Coast may be expected to decline sharply while that of the Gulf states increases. Only time will tell the correctness of this hypothesis.

Hurricane damage comes from wind, rain, and pressure differences engendered by the tremendous quantities of shifting air and water. The fierce gusts of a hurricane are equivalent to impacts of up to one hundred pounds on every square foot of exposed surface. Under such hammering, buildings disintegrate. Objects ripped off and carried by the wind become projectiles or battering rams. Trains have been blown off their tracks and heavy fortress cannons from their mounts. In temperate zones a rainfall of one inch per storm is considered heavy. Hurricanes have been known to loose deluges of an inch an hour for twenty-four hours. Once, in the Philippines, forty-six inches fell in twenty-four hours; in Jamaica, ninety-six and one-half inches were recorded in one four-day period. In addition, coastal areas may be inundated by waves of water driven by a hurricane's winds. Surging against the shore at up to forty miles per hour, the waves sweep over low-lying areas and breach all but the strongest sea walls. Because of the rising air currents, a large hurricane may reduce the air load on a square mile of land by as much as two million tons, while nearby the surging sea loads the bottom with a net extra weight of several million tons per square mile. The sudden application of such shifting loads may be sufficient to trigger earthquakes in an area where earth faults occur. A disastrous earthquake in Japan in 1923, for example, is believed to have been precipitated by a hurricane.

To reduce hurricane damage as much as possible, the United States government maintains a hurricane radar network from Texas to Maine, and military installations overseas also have radar equipment that is capable of tracking the storms [Plate 2]. Into the Weather Bureau Forecast Center in Washington goes weather information from these stations, as well as radio reports from hundreds of coastal stations, weather balloons, ships, and planes. From the Center, when a hurricane appears, the latest information about location, wind speeds, course, and all the other pertinent data go out to news-distributing and broadcasting services, Air Force bases, Navy bases, and the like. The information is also fed into electronic calculators, from which, aided by a mass of data on the behavior of previous hurricanes, comes a report on how the hurricane is behaving and is expected to behave.

Planes that probe the hurricane are flying laboratories bristling with instruments. For altitudes between 1000 and 25,000 feet, B-50 bombers are used; between 30,000 and 45,000 feet, B-47 jet bombers get the job. The balloons that test the storm are ingenious devices themselves. One type is designed to be dropped in the hurricane's eye, where it will then float serenely, radioing its position, thus the position of the hurricane. A rocket base near Norfolk, Virginia, has been readied to fire camera-equipped two-stage rockets some one hundred miles above the first hurricane that comes within range to give a panoramic view of the entire storm.

While the power of a hurricane is truly awesome, no atmospheric disturbance equals a tornado for concentrated fury. To the interior of North America belongs the unenviable distinction of being the area of the globe most frequented by these demons of destruction. Although tornadoes occur over all the continents, their appearance is rare except in the United States and Australia. Australian tornadoes are about as frequent as ours, but less severe. During this century an average of some two hundred tornadoes has been reported in the United States, but, probably because of better detection and reporting, 1957 saw two and one-half times that number and 1958 nearly five times the previous average. They have been reported in all of the forty-eight states. They occur in every month: most in May, fewest in December.

A tornado, often called a "prairie twister" and sometimes miscalled a cyclone, is an intense, spiral air motion around a vertical or inclined axis, generally about 250 yards across. At one time it was thought the winds dropped sharply outside this zone, but we now suspect that strong circulation prevails for a considerable distance beyond the visible funnel. Characteristically a tornado appears as a narrow cloud hanging from a higher cloud base reaching to, or nearly to, the ground (Plate 3). Sometimes the cloud dwindles to ropelike thinness; sometimes it is larger at the bottom than at the top, like a tree trunk; but most often it looks like a gigantic elephant's trunk, perhaps a mile long, dangling from the heavens. Most frequently its color is gray, its appearance being due to condensed water vapor. Sometimes it seems to be quite black, as if composed of tar. When the writhing tip contacts the ground, the tornado's appearance is considerably modified by the dust and debris picked up. On rare occasions tornadoes are completely invisible; in the winter they have been observed to descend on a field of snow and become dazzling white.

Tornadoes spring into life with diabolical suddenness. They are apparently produced from a variety of conditions, although generally they originate from the collision of a mass of warm, humid, southerly air with another cooler, drier air mass from more northerly areas. The warm air layer is usually 8000 to 10,000 feet thick and the cool air moves in at an elevation of 5000 to 6000 feet. By so doing an upper stratum of warm air is lifted and a sandwich of warm, then cool, then again warm air results. Extreme turbulence develops along the air mass boundaries. An eddy occasionally grows into a strong whirl through which the warmer air escapes upward like a beach ball from under an unsteady swimmer.

To other air moving laterally into the area of the vertical breakthrough, the earth's rotation imparts a swirl. Just as an ice skater twirls more rapidly or a ballet dancer pirouettes faster and faster as the arms are drawn toward the body, so the air whirls with greater velocity as it approaches the breach. Upon ascending, it expands and cools, and cooling causes condensation, releasing latent heat energy. This energy helps to maintain and to intensify the whirling. Whether or not condensation is the primary source of energy is a much debated point. As long ago as 50 B.C. the Roman Lucretius attributed tornadoes to the vivid electrical displays associated with them. The idea has recently been revived, but just how a tornado can utilize electrical energy has not been determined. The initial stages of tornado formation most likely do not involve electrical phenomena. Once the tornado is established as a vortex in the atmosphere, it may be that it then becomes intensified by electrical heating or electrical-wind effects.

Tornadoes move generally from southwest to northeast in the Northern Hemisphere, although there is nothing consistent about their movement. They have been known to move in circles and figure eights, to make U turns, and to stand still. They may roar across country at speeds up to 130 miles an hour, but the average speed is nearer 25 miles an hour. They last longest and travel straightest over flat, open country, although here the pendulous funnel may sway from side to side and bounce up and down. Hills, large buildings, and other wind barriers are apt to deflect their course, and by this agency new twisters are sometimes produced. Contrary to what might be the expected behavior, the windward sides of hills and even hilltops are less vulnerable than secluded valleys. Tornadoes seem to have as natural an inclination for dipping into valleys as children have for reaching into a bag of candy. Fortunately, the swath a tornado cuts across country is relatively small. The width of its path varies from a few feet to a couple of miles, and, on the average, a tornado sweeps an area less than twenty-five miles long. The average tornado life spans only about eight minutes, and of this only fifteen seconds is visited on any one spot. But few tornadoes are average. One granddaddy ravaged the countryside for seven hours, traveling nearly three hundred miles.

Before a tornado, the humidity is high and the air is hot and oppressive. Oftentimes it has been so for days. A gentle wind may have been blowing from the south, but, as it dies away, the heat and oppressiveness are intensified. A line of thunderheads, at first low on the horizon, appears in the west. It rises swiftly to dominate the sky.

A most lucid and graphic account of a tornado was given by a Kansas farmer, Will Keller, who escaped unscathed even though a tornado passed directly over him. About four o'clock on the afternoon of June 22, 1928, Keller noticed greenish black clouds in the southwest. Suspecting a tornado, he watched and soon could see that not one but three tornadoes had developed. Two looked like ropes hanging from the clouds, but the closest, the one bearing down upon him, had a real funnel shape. After hurrying his family into their cyclone cellar, Keller stopped in the doorway for one last look.

He saw the cloud coming steadily on and saw that the end was rising gradually above the ground. In what seemed like a long time but probably was only a few seconds, Keller realized that the great funnel was hanging directly over him. All wind had ceased, and a pungent odor prevailed. A screaming, screeching sound poured from the end of the funnel, and Keller, to his astonishment, could see up into the very interior of the vortex. The circular opening, which he judged to be between fifty and one hundred feet across and to extend upward at least one-half mile, was brilliantly lighted by lightning zigzagging from side to side. Small twisters formed and writhed their way around inside the rim of the tornado.

A similar experience with a Texas tornado was had by Roy S. Hall, a retired U. S. Army Captain, in May, 1948, and his description of the inside of the funnel—the flashing lightning giving a shimmering fluorescent glow, the terrific whirling, and the horrendous roar—is almost identical with the earlier description. In one respect, however, Hall's report adds a very interesting detail. As he looked up into the funnel, it appeared that the whole column was composed of rings or layers mounted one on top of the other much in the manner of a stack of automobile tires at a service station. If a higher ring moved laterally, the ring immediately below slipped over to a position underneath again, and this rippling motion continued down the funnel. When the motion had progressed the entire length, the lowest segment tilted and with a jerk flicked away a neighbor's house in this particular instance.

The roar of an approaching tornado is deafening. The sound has been described as ten thousand trains passing in the night, a million bulls bellowing at once, and the chorus of a squadron of jet planes. So intense is the roar that the crashing of buildings and the destruction of trees is unnoticed. The awesome effect is frequently accompanied by a thunderstorm and deluges of rain or hail. Lightning, as described, often plays along the tornado's funnel.

The swirling winds are so fantastically violent that no instrument to measure their velocity has yet survived their direct fury. Indirect evidence and theoretical calculations place highest wind velocity between two and eight hundred miles per hour. When a tornado struck in Worcester County, Massachusetts, in June, 1953, transmission-line towers were destroyed, affording, perhaps, one of the best estimates of actual velocity. The design of these towers, at the time of their construction, had been carefully tested by engineering methods. From the damage to them, the speed of the wind was estimated to have been at least 335 miles per hour but not greater than 375 miles per hour. Other estimates from tornado effects have given wind velocities greater than 500 miles per hour. These higher figures are subject to considerable uncertainty, however.

Whatever their actual speed, tornadic winds are truly fantastic. Some of the effects caused by them would be unbelievable had they not been photographed and observed by so many. In the furious winds, normally harmless and even fragile objects become missiles with great penetrating power. Cornstalks have been forced into doors, trees, and fence posts. Wheat straws have been driven into tree trunks to a depth exceeding one-half inch. A corn cob once pierced a horse's skull. Wooden sticks have been driven through iron plates; larger pieces of timber through brick walls; and, in one case, a pine pole was driven completely through an eighteen-inch trunk of a poplar tree.

Updrafts of air of tremendous force are created within a tornado's funnel, and the skies' giant vacuum cleaner has levitated an assortment of objects. Large iron bridges have been wrenched from their foundations and dropped in a crumpled heap some distance away. Automobiles and railroad cars have been whisked away; even railroad cars loaded with brick have been overturned. Roofs and church spires have been transported a dozen miles. In one Kansas tornado a herd of steers, looking like a flight of gigantic birds, was carried far overhead. Animals and human beings have been carried great distances and then set down unhurt. In 1955 at Bowdle, South Dakota, a mother saw a tornado lift her nine-year-old daughter and the pony the little girl was riding into the air. As the horrified mother watched, the pair were carried, spinning end over end, for half a mile. Still astride the pony when they were put down, the little girl was battered and bruised but did not require hospitalization. The pony was not injured.

That any living thing can be carried to great heights and then not be dashed to death when finally dropped arouses doubts in even the most credulous persons. The fact is that the tornado's victims are not dropped, but are lowered through an ascending air current. If they fell from the heights to which tornadoes may carry them—perhaps as much as a mile—they would certainly suffer serious injury if not instant death. It will be remembered, however, that a tornado is produced from a rising current of air, a wind blowing upward. The wind outside the funnel, while not as great as that near the tornado center that first carried the object into the air, nevertheless may be great enough to produce rather large buoyant effects. It is this wind that lowers objects back to earth.

The suction that is found in the maw of a tornado causes corks to pop from bottles, trunks to fly open, clothing to be stripped from human beings, chickens to be completely denuded of feathers, and houses to explode. The normal pressure of the atmosphere, it will be recalled, amounts to nearly fifteen pounds on each square inch of area, the force being applied equally on the outside as well as the inside of a dwelling, for example. In a tornado's funnel this pressure may be reduced between three and four pounds. As the tornado strikes, the air trapped inside a room suddenly finds itself opposed by a diminished force on the outside. A pressure difference of four pounds per square inch means that an average window is subjected to several tons, a wall to perhaps a hundred tons, and a house to thousands of tons of explosive force.

The tornado has two cousins, the waterspout and the dust devil. Neither, fortunately, is as fierce as its unholy relative. The waterspout is a marine tornado [Plate 3]. In shape and appearance it is very much like a tornado, a snakelike cloud that writhes and dips toward the sea. As the lower tip of the cloud approaches the surface, the water churns and appears to boil upward. When at last the rising cone of water and the cloud tip meet, a cascade of spray much wider than the spout itself is produced. Waterspouts, though they have average winds of an estimated one hundred miles per hour, are much less dangerous than tornadoes. Occurring over the water wastes of the world, their energy is largely lost on the waves.

Dust devils are formed over sun-baked land. Because they do not manage to reach into sufficiently high and cold regions of the atmosphere to engender moisture condensation, that source of energy is denied them. The dust devil is thus relegated to the status of second cousin to the tornado. Dust devils are bred under a variety of atmospheric conditions, but they are thought usually to start from updrafts of heated air that are caught in the natural turbulence of the winds and sent spiraling on their way. Tiny whirlwinds may be seen over wheat fields and city streets on many summer afternoons. Lasting less than a minute, they do nothing but kick up a few leaves and dust. Occasionally one will grow energetic enough to tear a few shingles off a roof. The true dust devil is an inhabitant of the desert, the largest recorded one having occurred near Cairo, Egypt. It reached a mile in height and flailed about for nearly six hours. An average one has less than a tenth that height and is some one hundred feet across. They are easily distinguished from tornadoes because they appear to dance along the ground rather than to hang from a cloud.

Electronics seems to provide the best hope for locating tornadoes quickly and accurately, necessities where these dangerous and short-lived storms are concerned. Lightning flashes from tornado clouds send out sferics, atmospheric radio waves of unusually high frequency, that can be distinguished from ordinary thunderstorm sferics or static. Sferics detectors sweeping from thunderstorm to thunderstorm can locate those that may produce tornadoes in time to warn the local inhabitants of impending danger. Already radar is being used to track tornadoes after they have formed so that people in the projected path can be alerted. Such warning gives only a few minutes in which to seek shelter, but a Texas network is already credited with saving many lives, and similar protection is to be extended over other parts of the United States.

Hurricanes may be the most destructive storms and tornadoes the most furious, but thunderstorms are certainly the most common. Although they occur chiefly in warm climates and during the warm season in temperate zones, they are not foreign to polar regions. They attain their greatest number and severity in the tropics, however. Places in Java experience over three hundred yearly. Portions of tropical Africa and South America are visited by well over a hundred in the course of a year. In the United States, the South is the favorite battleground of thunderstorm clouds, Pensacola, Florida, leading with an average of nearly ninety a year.

Considering loss of life and property damage, thunderstorms, due to their wide distribution and frequent occurrence, are probably the most serious of all storms. Whereas a hurricane can be spotted days before it strikes, the thunderstorm is erratic. That thunderstorms will develop in the afternoon is almost certain when a summer morning dawns hot, hazy, and humid, but where they will strike cannot be predicted. In one locality the sun may be shining, while only a few miles away the winds may be uprooting trees and unroofing houses.

Two types of thunderstorms are recognized. One is the self-contained disturbance that grows within a warm air mass. It occurs generally in the latter part of a summer afternoon, after the earth's surface has become its hottest. The other forms along the forward edge of a cool air mass as it penetrates over a warmer region. The latter can occur at any time of year; when lightning and thunder are seen and heard during a winter's night, a cold front is certainly passing over.

Thunderstorms require warm and humid air; they form most readily when there is little wind. In time, of course, the thunderstorm will create its gusts and squalls, but in its early stages winds disrupt the vertical currents from which the disturbance is bred. As in the case of other storms, the trigger that starts the thunderstorm is air that has been heated by the sun's rays. Over land, unlike water, heating is uneven. A cornfield gets warmer than a similar area of wooded land; a valley heats differently from hilly terrain. Warmest portions of air tend to rise, and, once started on their journey, they shoot up with ever accelerating speeds. Air from nearby areas is drawn into the rising current until, within the space of ten minutes, a cell of air perhaps three miles in diameter and three or more miles high is moving upward. The cell as it boils up is visible as the familiar thunderhead.

In the upper portions of the cloud the updrafts may attain a speed of thirty-five miles per hour. An airplane flying through it finds the air turbulent and bumpy. On the ground the inflow of air produces a slight wind. If it happens that a light prevailing wind is blowing over the area where the thunderstorm is developing, the winds will tend to cancel each other on one side of the storm and give the well-known "calm before the storm."

As the rising air moves into higher and cooler altitudes, moisture begins to condense as raindrops. Above the freezing level, three or four miles up, snow prevails. Soon the updrafts become unable to sustain the increasing weights of rain and snow. As this load plummets earthward it drags along part of the air of its environment and initiates a reverse movement within the cell, a downdraft. The downdraft brings rain to the land beneath; in a severe thunderstorm, hail may fall. The descending cool air from above causes the temperature to drop, a familiar characteristic of a thunderstorm. The updrafts and downdrafts produce wind gusts averaging maybe fifty miles per hour along the ground, and lightning plays about in the cloud. This, the mature stage of a thunderstorm, lasts from fifteen to thirty minutes.

The downdraft continues to grow at the expense of the upward currents. When it has spread completely across the cell, the supply of air entering to feed the storm is cut off. Condensation in the upper levels of the cell ceases, the downdraft decreases in speed, and turbulence dies away. The downpour that prevailed at the height of the storm declines to a light, steady rain that may linger for several minutes. Then the clouds dispel, the sun breaks through, and the atmosphere recovers its composure.

Thunderstorm activity usually covers a rather large area, sometimes more than two hundred square miles. The individual cells, however, like the one described, are rarely more than three miles wide. The several cells in one storm area may be and usually are in different stages of development at one time. This cellular characteristic as well as the development within each cell is readily recognizable to an observer on the ground, once he understands the thunderstorm's make-up. From a distance, separate rain areas, denoting cells, may be visible beneath the general cloud base. If a cell that has already reached the raining stage drifts over, a marked increase in wind gustiness, due to the outflowing downdraft, will be noticed just before the rain arrives. A decided decrease in ambient temperature will also accompany the wind. If a cell reaches the raining stage immediately overhead, there will be a moment of almost breathless calm followed by rain and the cool downdraft. Should the cell pass close by, the refreshingly cool winds of the downdraft may be felt even if no rain falls.

Though man has split the atom, blasted islands from the sea, and ringed the earth with artificial moons, his best present recourse before the storms that darken the skies is to run and hide. To determine when to hide is the object of much present endeavor, but so also is an understanding of precisely how storms are hatched, how they develop, and where is their Achilles' heel. Someday research may remove all storms' sting; but that day, as revealed in more detail in Chapter 11, is just dawning.

6 electricity in the sky

I saw the lightning's gleaming rod
Reach forth and write upon the sky
The awful autograph of God.
                          JOAQUIN MILLER

THE LIGHTNING's flash lasts less than a thousandth of a second, yet it is the result of a complex series of events and, with the millions of other flashes that play between the sky and the earth each day, is evidence of electricity throughout the atmosphere. Being one of nature's most spectacular phenomena, lightning has stirred man's fears and imagination since the dawn of history. Although we know the lightning now to be directed neither by demons nor displeased gods, it is not something to be regarded casually; it arises from the interplay of vast electric forces in the atmosphere and itself represents the greatest concentration of power in nature. Lightning is, however, only one aspect of atmospheric electricity. We are quite unaware of much of the electric drama that goes on about us.

In effect, the earth is one electrode of a gigantic electric-generating station, and the ionosphere, the electrically conducting layer of the upper atmosphere (Chapter 3), is the other. The earth normally is charged hundreds of thousands of volts negative with respect to the ionosphere. Since we occupy space between the two electrodes and thus are subject to a portion of their difference, our heads actually poke into a region that is two hundred volts more positive than our feet, even on the prettiest days. During foggy weather the difference may increase to a value ten times as great. In dust storms of the type common in semiarid and desert regions it may rise to three thousand volts for each vertical foot, or some eighteen thousand volts between the level of a man's head and the ground. In cloudy and rainy weather, the effects are highly variable, ranging from a few hundred to as much as fifteen thousand volts per foot.

This erratic behavior of electricity in the atmosphere results from a tug-of-war between two mechanisms, one generating electricity and the other draining the electricity away. The former is a powerhouse of remarkable capabilities, for our earth's charge would completely disappear in perhaps an hour if it were not continuously replenished. Yet the charge persists, and there are indications that its pattern has not changed significantly during geologic times. Clearly also, an equally versatile system permits the charges to escape. Thunderstorm activity is the power station in the sky; the charges are led away by invisible air molecules, called ions, which, having lost or gained an electron, are carriers of minute amounts of electricity.

Each thunderstorm produces electricity at a fantastic rate, differences of hundreds of millions of volts developing between the storm's upper and lower portions. Since each of the six to eight thousand individual thunderstorms, or thunderstorm cells, that are occurring more or less continuously over the earth's surface lasts about an hour, there are as many as 200,000 thunderstorms in each twenty-four-hour period. From all these storms there are probably more than 100 lightning flashes each second, or more than 300,000 in an hour. Every stroke sends currents, predominantly negative ones, into the earth. Equivalent positive currents, or charges, flow upward from the thunderstorms into the ionospheric storehouse.

Yet as soon as the thunderstorm passes, the earth's charge begins to steal away slowly and silently, riding on the omnipresent ions, which number about 150,000 per cubic inch of air. Compared to the millions upon billions of ordinary air molecules in such a volume, even this number is almost insignificantly small, but it is sufficient to make the air behave as a conductor nonetheless. Although they are not produced uniformly, ions are continuously formed in the atmosphere by a variety of processes involving radioactive substances which occur to some extent everywhere in the earth's solid crust, radioactive gases which emanate into the air from the ground, cosmic rays, the sun's ultraviolet light, and lightning itself. Near the earth, radioactive substances cause most of the ionization. A mile or so overhead and over the oceans, cosmic rays are the predominant influence since natural radioactivity is negligible there.

Being feebly charged themselves, ions are attracted or repelled by other charges much as an ordinary steel magnet attracts or repels another magnet. When a positive ion, for example, finds itself in the upper atmosphere, it is drawn toward the earth by the earth's negative charge. Similarly, a negative ion near the ground is propelled upward. When either reaches the object of its attraction or collides with an oppositely charged ion during the migration, a tiny fraction of the earth's charge will be dissipated by an exchange of electrons. This drama, enacted billions of times on a world-wide, around-the-clock schedule, never quite achieves electric neutrality for the earth. As pointed out, it would do so in approximately an hour if all lightning were to cease. But, even as freshly deposited charges are being drained away, other thunderstorms are marching across the land, pumping more charges into the earth.

Electricity generation, whether in a dynamo or in a thunderstorm, requires some means for separating positive and negative charges. Separation is accomplished in thunderclouds by their rising air currents, but precisely how has not been established, for the electric configuration of thunderclouds is so extraordinarily complex that it has defied complete analysis. Surprisingly, finding an electrification mechanism is not the problem; it is selecting the proper process from many possibilities that causes the difficulties. Very probably more than one mechanism operates in most thunderstorms. Since many raindrops start as tiny ice crystals, some undoubtedly bump into other ice crystals as they fall. When they reach lower and warmer altitudes they melt. Both as ice crystals and as raindrops they encounter a Sunday driver's nightmare of ion traffic during the descent. The winds distort and tear at them. The freezing, the melting, the collisions, the ions, and the wind-produced break-up possibly all contribute to charge generation.

A lightning-generating mechanism of considerable importance appears to be connected with the freezing process. It has been shown in the laboratory that a charge difference of several volts exists between ice and water in contact if very small amounts of impurities are present. Experiments have also shown that, when water drips on a piece of ice, a charge difference is developed if the water is a tiny bit impure. Most impurities in the air, and therefore to be found in rain, cause the ice to become negative and the water positive. This suggests that some thunderstorm electricity comes about when an ice particle that formed high in the cloud begins to fall. As it does so it is subjected to rising temperatures, and eventually it encounters water droplets near the freezing levels. Some of these collide with the ice particle, a portion of the water freezing about the particle and the remainder splashing away. In accordance with the laboratory findings, the ice particle becomes negative in the process while the water takes on positive charges. The ice particle gains weight from the encounter and falls even faster. The water left over, being split into smaller droplets, is carried higher by the rising air currents. As the ice falls farther and farther it too melts, and thereafter collisions with other droplets serve only to reduce its charge. The important feature of this process is that it permits charged zones, negative near the cloud's base and positive toward its upper extremity, to develop in thunderclouds in accordance with observed conditions.

But it is also observed that lightning can play among clouds that are everywhere above freezing temperatures. Clearly ice formation cannot enter here. It is probable that ion capture by falling raindrops is of importance instead. A peculiar property of ions is that at some elevations the positive ones seem to be larger than the negative ones, and hence sluggish and lazy in comparison to their smaller negative counterparts, while at other levels the reverse is the case. This makes collisions between raindrops and one kind of ion more likely at each particular level and probably contributes to charge generation, particularly in early phases of thunderstorm development.

Other processes can occur once the thundercloud has reached a stage of development such that it has pronounced charged zones. These raise the charges to still higher levels. For example, a raindrop, even though neutral as a whole, has charges induced on it as a result of the cloud's charges. Induced charges are those that always appear on any body not in contact with, but exposed to, another charged object, the nearest part taking on a charge opposite to that of the object. The underside of each raindrop, if the lower portion of the cloud is negative, thus takes on an induced positive charge, while the top of the raindrop gets a negative charge from the upper parts of the cloud. When the raindrop falls, the induced positive charge on its leading surface forces positive ions in its path aside but gathers in the negative ones, since opposite charges attract and like charges repel each other. A sizable net negative charge is probably carried by this means to the lower portions of a thundercloud. The rebuffed positive ions accumulate at higher elevations.

The latter process, like a blindly obedient genie, piles up charges in whatever direction they are started. Most thunderclouds are observed to have negative bottoms and positive tops, although this is by no means universal. The reverse is observed in about 5 per cent of the cases, and thunderclouds having three zones of charge, positive on top, negative in the middle, and positive again on the bottom, are common in some parts of the world.

Just as a thundercloud induces charges on the individual rain-drops, charges are induced on the earth beneath the cloud. If the underside of the thundercloud is negative, a positive charge accumulates on that portion of the earth immediately below; or, if the cloud base is positive, the earth underneath becomes even more negative than ordinarily. This zone of induced charges glides along like a shadow—an electric shadow, to be sure—under the thundercloud.

Normally atmospheric electricity is carried rather leisurely, as we have seen, an electron at a time, by the multitude of ions in the air. When thunderclouds are abroad, however, charge differences between the clouds and the earth are much greater than they ever are between the earth and the ionosphere, and the ions caught between the thundercloud and the earth are forced to move more rapidly. When the charge difference between the earth and the cloud reaches something of the order of one hundred million volts, nearly one million times our ordinary house voltage, the ions attain such a state of frenzy that collisions between them and normal air molecules produce other ions more rapidly than ions are destroyed in the encounters. Like a runaway nuclear reaction, a breakdown of the air's resistance follows and the electrical storehouse of the cloud is emptied, or partially emptied, by a violent discharge, the lightning.

To our naked eyes, lightning appears to be a single flash. As in so many other cases, however, scientific investigation has revealed much more about the lightning stroke than is commonly visible. High-speed photography has been particularly valuable in clarifying the nature of a lightning stroke. In the camera used for this purpose the lens moves rapidly, and the events thus photographed are progressively displayed in positions relative to their time of occurrence. Events only one one-millionth of a second apart can be detected in this fashion.

A lightning stroke does not happen all at once. First the path along which the main current will later flow is established. This is accomplished by streams of ions that surge forth from the cloud base toward the ground when the cloud voltage reaches the critical value. These burrow through the air, building an ionized or electrically conducting bridge as they go. They proceed in an irregular, stepwise fashion; after each hundred feet or so the ion streams temporarily lose their drive and halt much as an army does when it must recoup its losses and plan the next attack. A fresh direction of travel is usually followed after each hesitation, giving rise to the tortuous path that lightning displays. Each halt in the march, while readily discernible in a high-speed photograph, really lasts only a few millionths of a second. The entire trip of the preparatory streamers between cloud and earth requires, maybe, one one-hundredth of a second. As these streamers near the ground by their process of advance and consolidation, opposite charges on the earth crowd into the area of approach. The charge intensity on the ground then becomes so great that other streamers surge upward from elevated areas and projections on the ground.

When a descending streamer contacts an ascending one, a violent torrent of electricity—the lightning—flashes along the path thus established, at a speed of some sixty thousand miles per second. The whole streamer channel is brilliantly lighted as the energy drains from the cloud into the earth. The rushing currents also generate heat, sound, and electromagnetic waves, the latter familiar as static on radio receivers. A single stroke may not drain off all of a thundercloud's energy; in this case other strokes follow along the same channel in rapid succession until the cloud's charges are temporarily depleted. In a rather active thunderstorm separate lightning discharges flash about every twenty seconds, but flashes may occur much more rapidly, even simultaneously from different parts of a thunderstorm [Plate 3].

The actual lightning channel is generally between one and four inches wide, the evidence being the diameter of holes punched in objects or the width of burned streaks left on them by lightning strikes. The electrical energy expended by an average thundercloud giving a stroke every twenty seconds amounts to a rate of a million kilowatts continuously. Some 25,000 amperes are carried by an average stroke; often it reaches 60,000; and one stroke of more than 300,000 amperes was registered. The last carried energy sufficient to light momentarily about 600,000 sixty-watt bulbs, while a single average lightning stroke could power several thousand television sets for one hour.

Such amounts of energy concentrated in short bursts are capable of prodigious feats. Trenches are sometimes plowed in the earth by lightning. Trees, telephone poles, and chimneys are splintered or shattered when they are a part of the lightning's path. The splitting of trees is thought to be due to the current's dissociating the moisture in the tree into hydrogen and oxygen, which on ignition by the heat of the lightning react with explosive violence. The temperature of the lightning channel itself probably rises to 50,000 degrees on the Fahrenheit scale. Metal objects, like wires, pipes, or conduits, having no gaseous components, are sometimes heated to such temperatures that they vaporize completely. The metal centers of rubber-covered outdoor telephone lines have been known to disappear completely, leaving the rubber apparently undamaged. Probably this happens because the copper center, being a good conductor of heat, is vaporized before the rubber, a rather poor conductor, gets hot. In the same vein, the story is told of a lady closing a window during a thunderstorm. There was a flash of lightning and her gold bracelet vanished, leaving a blue circle, an oxide of gold, about her wrist, but not a burned arm.

The thunder that follows the lightning is produced by the terrific heat of the discharge causing the air to expand with the violence of an explosion. When the lightning is close, the sound is often one sharp and uncomfortable crack. Since a lightning stroke may be a mile or more long and sound travels at a comparatively slow speed, the thunder can last for several moments, the sound first heard coming from the near part of the flash and that heard after a lapse of some time coming from a more distant part. The uneven character or rumbling of thunder may be due to any of several factors. The branching and multiple nature of some strokes produces sounds from more than one locality as well as at different times. These can arrive so as to reinforce each other, thereby causing a particularly loud noise, or at different times, prolonging the sound. Echoes help to produce the rolling effect of thunder, especially in mountainous areas.

Lightning can show hues of many colors. The usual white is produced because the terrifically strong electric currents cause the very atoms of oxygen and nitrogen to radiate visible light in much the same way that rarefied neon gas glows in a glass tube under moderate electrification. It so happens that combination of the spectra of oxygen and nitrogen gives a white light. When water vapor is ionized, adding the spectrum of the element hydrogen, reddish or pinkish coloring is evident. When the air is heavily charged with dust, yellow or red flashes may be seen. Violet and green lightning have been reported, but such colored flashes are rare.

Lightning does not always play between the clouds and the earth. Discharges also take place between two clouds and between different parts of the same cloud. Usually cloud-to-cloud lightning must jump great distances, ten to twenty miles not being uncommon. One flash of thirty miles was recorded photographically. Cloud-to-earth flashes rarely exceed one mile in length, and when thunderclouds pass over high mountains, flashes of only a hundred yards sometimes occur. The areal illumination often referred to as heat or sheet lightning, which plays along the horizon on sultry summer evenings, is very probably cloud-to-cloud lightning, occurring beyond the horizon out of range of direct sight and too distant for its thunder to be audible.

Lightning and its accompanying phenomena are worth understanding for one very practical reason, if for no other: a knowledge of lightning's characteristics could save your life. If everyone knew and practiced caution, the five hundred or so deaths and many hundred injuries that occur each year in this country alone from lightning could be virtually eliminated. In view of the fact that ground streamers—which, it will be recalled, become the lower terminus of a lightning stroke—rise from protruding structures and elevated locations, common sense tells one to stay away from elevated positions and exposed, projecting objects when thunderstorms are about. A tree on a hill is especially inviting to lightning, but a lone tree in a level field is also dangerous. Any tree, in fact, is an unsafe shelter in a thunderstorm. Golf courses are notoriously dangerous, as an upright person in an open area is himself a convenient terminus for a lightning discharge. Depressions in the ground—ditches and the like—provide the only really safe places in the open. Contrary to popular opinion, one is probably safer after being drenched by rain than before. Whether wet or dry, a man is not likely to survive a direct lightning stroke, but if lightning hits close when the clothing is wet, some of the current that otherwise might flow through the body will be carried by the water in the garments.

Injury by lightning arises from several effects. The blast of compressed air arising from the extreme temperature of the lightning can knock a man many feet. The electric shock produces sudden contraction of the arteries and the heart. The muscles of the limbs also contract violently. If there is any life left after the shock, artificial respiration applied immediately can drive blood from the lungs back into the heart and set it beating again. One woman who miraculously was not killed by lightning reported later that she first heard a terrific blast and then the lightning, looking like a beam of light, ran past; something finally pushed her off her feet and hurled her into the air. The "something" was the compression wave caused by the heat of the stroke.

During a thunderstorm, indoors is always safer than outdoors. One should avoid the immediate vicinity of a fireplace, however, since lightning usually hits the chimney, the highest part of most houses, and has been known to run down it, cross inside the room, and finally make contact with a radiator or similar object on its way to the earth. Inside an automobile, except possibly an open convertible, is a safe place. Should lightning strike a car, the metal frame would conduct the current around the occupants. Tall buildings are often struck; the Empire State Building has been hit innumerable times, its metal framework conducting the current harmlessly to the ground; occasionally, however, chunks of masonry and other debris are showered into the streets below following a stroke. This one example alone destroys the superstition of lightning's never striking twice in the same place. Actually lightning hits the highest, best-conducting object in the immediate vicinity, without regard for past occurrences.

Modern all-metal aircraft are inherently safe even though they occasionally pass through active thunderclouds and are sometimes struck. The metal surface and structure of the plane, like those of an automobile, form a path through which lightning currents are carried safely around occupants in the interior. However, certain external parts of aircraft, such as movable flight-control surfaces, plastic sections, and antennas, have been damaged. Boats, particularly sailboats, are struck frequently. In fact, any protrusion above the level surface of the sea is a likely target. Swimmers are sometimes killed, more often badly shocked when lightning strikes the water. If one is swimming or boating when a thunderstorm approaches, he should get out of the water. All-metal ships are safe for the same reason that cars and airplanes are safe, the metal furnishing a path for the current. Before the advent of metal construction, however, ships suffered heavily from lightning damage.

Perhaps nothing associated with lightning has been the subject of more arguments or the focus of greater prejudices than lightning rods, yet since their invention they have saved countless lives and many millions of dollars' worth of property. In the first place, the lightning rod's purpose was repugnant because it seemed to contradict a deep-seated belief in the diabolical agency manifest in storms, once expressed in the words, "It is as impious to ward off God's lightnings as for a child to resist the chastening rod of the father." This feeling seems to have been particularly strong in medieval Europe, where it is shown by the plight of the bell-ringer especially. About the time of Charlemagne the practice of ringing church bells during lightning storms began. The origin of the custom is uncertain, but it may have been an outgrowth of the ringing of bells to signal the approach of any impending danger, including storms, and then gradually took on the significance of driving storms away. At any rate, bell-ringing during thunderstorms became quite common and notoriously hazardous as well. The bells were usually located in tall spires, the highest point of the church, which was itself located in a prominent, exposed position. The bell-ringer, of course, pulled a rope fastened directly to the bell at the top of the spire. If lightning struck, a very likely path to the earth was down the rope and through the bell-ringer to the ground. The practice vanished only early in the twentieth century. How many paid with their lives for the custom will never be known, but it was reported in Germany in 1783 that over one hundred bell-ringers were killed by lightning in one thirty-three-year period.

Today, lightning rods are still not used as extensively as they might be. If properly installed and maintained, they could prevent at least 90 per cent of the fires ordinarily started by lightning. Lightning rods do not prevent lightning from striking, nor can they be said to attract lightning as popularly believed. The streamers that plow through the air establishing the lightning's path seem to contact the streamers reaching upward from the ground at no more than twenty feet above ground level if there are no trees or buildings near. A projecting object like a chimney or a tree, of course, permits the ground streamer to reach higher. The function of a lightning rod is to produce a higher streamer than any other object in the immediate vicinity, so that, when lightning approaches dangerously close to the building being protected, the lightning can be led harmlessly away. A good electricity conductor like a pencil-size copper rod can carry the lightning's current.

Often when the voltage difference between earth and sky is very high, as before a lightning flash, a corona discharge known as St. Elmo's fire forms about pointed objects such as tall trees, flagpoles, and lightning rods. The discharge is usually not visible in daylight, but at night it manifests itself as an eerie glow. It was frequently seen on the masts and rigging of sailing vessels in bygone days and derives its name from the guardian saint of Mediterranean sailors, St. Elmo, who lived in Italy some three hundred years after the time of Christ. Today it is often seen on airplane wings and propeller tips. It is common on high mountains when thunderclouds pass over their peaks, for the bottoms of the clouds are then close to the ground, making electric fields that produce point discharges exceptionally intense. In South America it manifests itself as the Andes glow, which is often mistaken by airplane pilots for distant forest fires. In the Alps, mountain climbers have reported very impressive crackling, luminous flames spouting from their heads and fingers. The glow about the head takes the form of a halo, and pointed objects such as ice axes seem to be tipped with flame. On our own western mountain ranges, steers occasionally seem to have flames leaping from their horns. It is quite possible that the flaming yet unconsumed bush that Moses encountered on Mount Sinai was due to the type of discharge that we now call St. Elmo's fire. This so-called fire has been seen running along the ground ahead of a tornado's funnel. The effect comes about because the intensification of the electric field near a point causes such a profusion of ions to be ejected that the surrounding air molecules glow under the intense bombardment; it is of the same nature as light from a neon sign. Of itself St. Elmo's fire is quite harmless, but it should be avoided because it indicates a point of great electric intensity and as such is a possible terminus for lightning flashes.

Dramatic lightning displays accompany other natural phenomena, though they are relatively insignificant insofar as the earth's and the atmosphere's charges are concerned. Tornadoes appear to have an electrical activity ten to twenty times greater than ordinary thunderstorms. On May 25, 1955, when a devastating tornado hit Blackwell, Oklahoma, the funnel was observed to glow, suggesting a beacon lamp in a lighthouse. This effect was probably produced by lightning playing inside the funnel. During volcanic eruptions the frictional rubbing together of great quantities of dust and ash often cause lightning to flash about the summit. Dust storms of the Sahara and elsewhere produce much lightning.

All of the consequences of atmospheric electricity are not readily apparent. As mentioned in the introductory chapter, lightning today produces nitrogen compounds in the air, which become valuable plant nutrients when brought down to the earth with rainfall. In the dim, distant past, when the earth's atmosphere was laden with hydrogen, methane, ammonia, and other vapors, lightning undoubtedly initiated the formation of many more compounds. It is just possible that lightning has had more to do with the development of life on this earth than we realize. The "spark of life" may well be an apt phrase!

The energy stored in the earth and ionosphere would certainly supply millions of horsepower continuously if it could be harnessed. When the ionosphere shifts, as it does daily under the influence of the sun's uneven heating, electric currents of the order of 100,000 amperes are generated by the dynamo action of the charges moving across the earth's magnetic field. At times when magnetic storms race round the earth, electrical energy equivalent to that obtainable from fifty thousand tons of coal is loosed in the atmosphere in a day's time. Except for the direct lightning, this energy is spread over very large geographical areas, so that the actual energy density is low. In the case of lightning itself, a vast network of some description would be necessary to capture its fleeting, though concentrated, energy. Some years ago a wire screen several hundred square yards in area was suspended from insulated cables between two mountain peaks in Switzerland and is said to have emitted an almost steady discharge of sparks fifteen feet long from its terminals. At the time it was maintained that charges of thirty million volts could be obtained with modifications to the apparatus. Even so, reducing this excessively high voltage to a usable level would be extremely difficult. Therefore, only one exceedingly bold would predict that a feasible way to fetter the lightning is likely to be found. It should be borne in mind, however, that atmospheric electricity will not be forgotten as new energy sources are sought in the future.

An accidental battlefield discovery of World War I revealed an odd effect of lightning which today is being used to probe the outermost limits of the atmosphere. A German physicist, while wire-tapping Allied field telephone conversations with probes stuck in the ground to pick up the minute electric currents leaking from Allied telephone wires, noticed that curious whistling sounds occasionally swamped the military chatter. Being unable to find any defect in his apparatus, he predicted, correctly as it turned out, that the sounds originated in the atmosphere, but many years elapsed before their source was established.

The first real clue developed when it was noticed that the "whistlers," as the sounds came to be called, were often preceded by a loud click. The click was soon related to electromagnetic waves—static, in the more familiar terminology—from nearby lightning flashes, and, after considerable detective work, the whistlers were related to other waves from the lightning stroke which, starting vertically outward, were bent by the earth's magnetic field so that they struck the earth at a corresponding point in the other hemisphere. Bouncing upward again, they return to their initial point of origin. When preceded by a click, a whistler comes from a nearby lightning flash, the waves of which traveled in a great arc reaching out from the earth as much as seven thousand miles to the other hemisphere and bounced back; when no click is heard, the whistler originated with a lightning stroke nearly half a world away. Thus lightning in New Zealand stamps its mark in the Aleutian Islands, and a New England thunderstorm reveals itself in southern Argentina.

So far we have dealt almost exclusively with events that take place between the lower portion of a thundercloud and the earth, because these are by far the best-understood phenomena. But by the inexorable laws of nature a quantity of electricity of equal magnitude and opposite sign must be sent upward for each quantity driven to the earth. How charges escape from the tops of thunderclouds into the upper air is a matter of much speculation. Even though there have been reports of lightning flashes leaping upward from the clouds, such discharges are very likely rare. Most probably, nonviolent discharges like St. Elmo's fire drive the currents upward. Supporting this view are well-established observations of glows above the tops of clouds. One remarkable case in point was a rather brilliant ball of light observed above a cloud bank in New Zealand, which pulsated in intensity and size for fifteen minutes while lighting up the tops of the clouds and even the countryside with a greenish white radiance. At other times glow discharges have been seen wreathing cloud tops when lightning flashes were striking toward the earth. Much more information on the behavior of this twin of lightning is sorely needed.

Finally, one other form of lightning must be mentioned: a mysterious phenomenon called ball lightning, which many authorities are inclined to dismiss as an optical illusion. On the other hand, there are a great number of accounts of the appearance of a moving fireball during thunderstorm periods. Such a ball is usually described as about eighteen inches across, though it may reach six feet. It is usually round and glows white, red, yellow, or blue. According to reports, it may persist from a few seconds to several minutes. It is generally said to bounce about or roll along the ground, but it has been seen to float in the air at times. Sometimes the balls are said to burst with sharp reports.

One typical account relates that during a thunderstorm a screen in front of a fireplace fell as if blown down by a wind. Then a yellowish ball appeared and floated in mid-air around the room. Although luminous, it did not seem to be hot. Eventually it passed out the chimney through which it entered and apparently exploded as it reached the top, for a shower of stones was thrown down from the chimney. This peculiar affinity for chimneys suggests that the phenomenon indoors is an extreme example of St. Elmo's fire about a cloud of soot or ashes raised from the hearth. Outdoors, it may be St. Elmo's fire about a cloud of dust or hailstones, or it may be a highly ionized pocket of air. Until the phenomenon can be produced artificially in the laboratory or until there are some really tangible observations, ball lightning must remain in an indefinite status.

7 vermin of the air

Have not the small particles of bodies
certain powers, virtues, or forces . . .
for producing a great part of the
phenomena of nature?

ISAAC NEWTON

THE AIR, free of clouds, palls of smoke, and banks of fog, is not the wholly gaseous realm it appears to be. It teems with invisible solid and semisolid bits of matter—viruses, spores, bacteria, pollen, smoke and dust particles. These, causing allergies, spreading diseases, and altering meteorological phenomena, exert an influence on the life of this globe that is comparable to that of the air itself.

Each bush, tree, or animal that dies decays eventually into dust, a portion of which is picked up by subsequent gusts of wind. Living trees, weeds, shrubs, and all manner of plant life shower little ball-like bits of matter called pollen into the air. Flooding rivers deposit fine silt, later to be scattered by the wind. The sea breaking on rocky shores flings up spray, which evaporates and leaves tiny salt crystals to be spread about the world. Volcanoes during eruptions discharge dust along with rock and lava. People, when they talk, cough, or sneeze, project microorganisms into the air. Forest fires and dust storms spread their airborne particles over millions of square miles. Even extremely fine dust born of meteoric disintegration falls through the atmosphere. Man's industrial activities are extremely potent producers of particle matter, but, being amenable to his control, will be considered in a later chapter dealing with the problem of atmospheric pollution.

Physically, chemically, and biologically there are great differences in the particle matter encountered in the air. Of most general importance, perhaps, are the size and the number of particles. Some wind-blown bits of matter are so large that they sting when they strike one's cheek. These seldom travel far before falling to the earth again. Finer particles may be carried miles before being dumped by a temporary lull in the wind. Still other material is so very fine that it remains suspended in the air indefinitely. Under the eternal bombardment of air molecules, and drifting with the slightest air currents, these finest particles are washed out only by the rain. Though the larger particles are annoying to get in one's eyes and particularly troublesome in great quantity, as in desert areas where drifts or dunes are produced, they are of relatively minor consequence insofar as the air is concerned because their tenure on wings is short. With the finer particles the story is quite different.

Hundredths and thousandths of an inch are large figures when air-borne particles are discussed. For convenience, scientists the world over who must deal with small quantities employ a unit of length called the *micron*, one one-thousandth of a millimeter, which is very nearly equal to four hundred-thousandths of one inch. The proverbial pinhole is about a thousand microns across, yet unaided good eyes can distinguish an isolated object fifty microns in diameter. Even so, the subjects of this chapter are ordinarily too small to be visible individually. Pollen grains come closest, being mostly above twenty-five microns across; spores, lying in the less-than-thirty-micron range, are hardly visible without microscopes. Dust and smoke particles are generally less than ten microns in diameter; bacteria are about one micron across; while virus particles amount only to very small fractions of one micron.

As with distance measured in light years or the national debt, we have difficulty in conceiving of the size of such particles. Perhaps a better idea of their minuteness can be gained by considering a group of particles suspended in one cubic inch of air, or about as much space as is occupied by a refrigerator ice cube. If in this one cubic inch there were scattered one million particles each one micron across, or the size of an average bacterium, the cube would still be nearly all air. In fact, much less than one one-millionth of the available space would be occupied by particles, and it would appear to be entirely empty except in the beam from a very bright light. Though hard to believe, it is true nevertheless that we could cup a million bacteria in our hands and never see them.

Particles, but fortunately not bacteria, are frequently encountered in concentrations as great as a million and a quarter in each cubic inch of air, but the number can drop as low as a hundred. Since, with normal activity, a human being's daily intake of air is about 400,000 cubic inches, this lowest figure means that a person inhales great numbers of foreign bodies each day; the highest, the astronomical figure of several hundred billion particles.

If our respiratory system were not remarkably conditioned to handle this debris, we would soon suffocate. When particles from the air enter the upper respiratory tract, they are selectively sifted. Those larger than about five microns are mostly strained from the air in the nasal passages; most of the finest particles are exhaled; but some of the matter is deposited in the air sacs of the lungs. Once deposited, one of three possible courses can then be followed: the particles can go into solution and be spread throughout the body, they can pass through the lung walls into the blood stream without dissolving, or they can remain in the lungs. If they dissolve, injurious reactions can be produced, should the material be toxic. Those that get into the blood stream unaltered are efficiently removed by the kidneys and liver; but in high concentration they can be harmful and even fatal. Those retained in the lungs produce a permanent tissue change called *fibrosis*, possibly the most dangerous condition of all. For example, prolonged breathing of insoluble rock dust causes the incurable disease silicosis. Until effective dust-suppression measures were undertaken in recent years, miners and rock-quarry workers were particularly susceptible to this malady.

Given time and still air, all but the smallest particles settle to the ground because of their own weight, and their rate of fall is closely related to particle size. A fog particle one hundred microns in diameter falls nearly a foot a second, whereas a ten-micron one falls only about one-tenth of an inch in the same time, and a one-micron droplet only little more than one one-thousandth of one inch. Its settling rate determines how far from its original sources a particle is likely to drift in the wind, and thus establishes the probable spread of particles from any source. The ten-micron particle, if it started from a height of, say, thirty feet and if the earth's surface were uniformly smooth, could be carried approximately six miles by a twenty-mile-an-hour wind. On the other hand a one-micron particle, under the same conditions, could span six hundred miles before touching down. Since most of the earth's terrain is irregular, and since upcurrents and downdrafts alternately spread and deposit some of the indifferent hitchhikers, particles may actually be transferred much greater or lesser distances.

For spread as well as for magnitude of air-borne dust, volcanic eruptions are unequaled. A particularly violent eruption puts unimaginable quantities of dust into the air, some of it to very high altitudes. In 1883, when the East Indian volcano Krakatoa vanished in the most violent eruption of modern times, several cubic miles of earth were disintegrated and belched into the air. Where a mountain 1400 feet high and covering 18 square miles had been, a crater 1000 feet deep was left. The dust from the explosion rose to a height of 17 miles and darkened the sky for 150 miles around. Days later, dust in such huge quantities settled on the decks of vessels 1600 miles distant that it had to be shoveled off several times. Again, following the eruption of the volcano Katmai, in Alaska, on June 6, 1912, great quantities of dust were produced. On Kodiak Island, 130 miles away, dust and ashes fell to a depth of nearly 18 inches. In both instances the finer dust was picked up by prevailing winds and spread around the world above the rains and storms that tend to cleanse the lower atmosphere, and a number of years elapsed before the effects of the dust entirely disappeared. Since it would take a two-micron dust particle something like four years to fall seventeen miles, the lingering effect is not in the least surprising.

In such cases when dust cloaks the earth, the world's weather seems to be affected. After Krakatoa, mean temperatures in the Northern Hemisphere averaged a couple of degrees lower for several years, and there was above-normal rain and snow. Following Katmai's eruption, a marked diminution in solar radiation reaching the earth was recorded, stations in California and Algeria reporting maximum diminutions of 23 per cent in August of that year. A change in the weather was more than mere coincidence, for, in addition to cutting off some of the sun's incoming heat, unusual quantities of dust in the air would be expected to increase precipitation, as we shall discuss more fully in a later chapter.

Dust storms also are prolific producers of air-borne dust. Periodically Europe is subjected to dust originating in the Sahara Desert. In March, 1901, an estimated two million tons fell on the European continent, and much more must have been deposited over the Mediterranean and beyond the continental limits. Almost two years later, in February, 1903, England alone received another deposit estimated at ten million tons. On many occasions, notably once in 1947, muddy rain and reddish snow have fallen on the southwestern part of Europe, Sahara dust again being the cause. Red dust particles appear in Florida's air occasionally, apparently from the Sahara also. Reddish snow has fallen in Greenland, of all places, while Iowa has reported pink snow and Kansas brown, dust being the cause in all cases. During the droughts of the 1930's, authorities believe that ten million tons of dust were air-borne at one time over our Midwestern states. High winds lifted this load more than a mile, then swept it along eighteen hundred miles in twenty-four hours. Whole states were clouded with a dull haze. Buffalo, New York, collected dust from north Texas, and the eastern seaboard from the Dakotas, during this period.

Turning from volcanoes and dust storms to the waters of the earth, we find still another potent source of air-borne particle matter. When the wind whips off the crest of an ocean wave or a ship flings spray from its bow, the finer droplets quickly evaporate, leaving tiny salt crystals. These the normal circulation of the winds carry over all the world. They are found thousands of miles from the nearest ocean and near the interior of most continents. Many instances of the air becoming heavily laden with salt particles have been recorded during gales. On one notable occasion trees and hedges 140 miles across England from the sea were encrusted with salt. Sometimes dry northeast winds blowing in on the New Jersey coast carry sufficient salt to short-circuit television antennas and power-line insulators. These are unusual events, however. Normally, salt particles from the sea are less than a micron in diameter. It would take a million billion of them to make a pound, but they play a very special part in weather processes. They are hygroscopic, meaning they have a distinct ability to take water from the air. In your kitchen salt shaker this is an undesirable trait, but in the atmosphere it means rain for crops, rivers, and waterfalls.

Each raindrop, whether from an April shower or a cloudburst, forms about a tiny particle. Each fog droplet and each cloud particle has at its center, or at least had before it dissolved, a particle of some type. Very likely it was a tiny crystal of sea salt, for these serve better than other natural substances found in the air. Dust and smoke particles, however, can become droplet nuclei if plentiful sea salt particles are not available.

The latter suggests that dust from meteor showers occasionally affects the rainfall throughout the world. It has been observed that maximum rainfall periods occur in both the Northern and Southern Hemispheres at about the same time. Such a world-wide rainfall peak has not been explained on a climatological basis, but, if the extraterrestrial influence is considered, a plausible explanation seems possible. When the earth, traveling in its orbit about the sun, encounters a swarm of meteors, each meteor striking the upper reaches of earth's atmosphere is ignited and burned by frictional heating so that the resulting debris is a fine smoke or powder. This "stardust" then floats down into the cloud system of the lower atmosphere, where it becomes nuclei upon which ice crystals or raindrops may form. Further confirmation that this actually happens is found in the fact, also observed, that the rainfall increase comes about a month after a particular meteor system is encountered, the delay being sufficient time to allow the meteoric dust to fall through the upper atmosphere. Occasionally large meteors leave a visible train of dust. Most often the trail disappears rapidly, but in a few witnessed cases it has remained visible for an hour or so. A great meteor that struck Siberia in 1908 and devastated an area of many square miles left a dust cloud behind it that traveled around the world before it dissipated.

Among the more spectacular producers of foreign matter in the air are large forest fires. Because of the violent updrafts of heated air created in such instances, smoke particles are carried to great heights, and, being small, are spread vast distances by the upper-air currents. In the fall of 1950 prolonged forest fires in Alberta, Canada, produced smoke that drifted over the eastern provinces, our eastern states, England, and finally the continent of Europe. The fires themselves were not particularly spectacular, but, being in swampy muskeg country, they gave off tremendous volumes of smoke, producing effects that were without parallel in remembered experience. A feeling of uneasiness, even near-panic, was felt by those affected as the smoke rolled in overhead during the daytime. At first the sky shone with an eerie sort of light, but in many areas almost total darkness followed. Afternoon sports events in Cleveland and Detroit were staged under floodlights as a result.

By a subtle scheme involving particles in the air, each forest fire creates the seeds of its own destruction. Burning wood produces, among other things, water vapor. The heat from a large conflagration like a forest fire causes mighty updrafts, which suck in surrounding air and carry it, its natural moisture, the water vapor produced by the fire, and the smoke in towering columns to high elevations. There the air is cooled, and there its moisture, if in sufficient quantity, condenses on particles to fall as rain, checking and occasionally putting out the fire [Plate 4].

Checks, balances, and built-in protection schemes are also a part of nature's plans to secure survival for her creations; unhappily one result is more particle matter in the air. Pollen, the male fertilizing element of most plants, is familiar as a fine yellowish powder in the center of a beautiful flower. Each pollen grain's mission is to seek out a female cell of its own species. Insects such as bees scatter some of it, but most of the dissemination is done by the winds. Floating aimlessly in the air, each grain has one chance in a billion of reaching its goal. With such odds against it, pollen is made plentiful. There are reports, for example, of lakes being covered with a yellow film of pollen at certain times of the year from trees that do not grow within hundreds of miles.

Unhappily, pollens pose a serious problem for millions of people. These allergic individuals have inherited a constitution that rebels against certain foreign intruders. When such substances are breathed, other substances called antibodies form in the lining membranes of the nose and throat, producing a reaction that irritates sensitive tissues of the eyes and the respiratory tract, the severity of the reaction depending upon the amount of pollen in the air and the length of the exposure. In severe cases the skin reacts also with red, swollen, itching eczema. Such allergy-caused ailments rank third among prevalent chronic diseases in this country; they exceed polio, arthritis, cerebral palsy, and multiple sclerosis combined. There are at least seven million persons in the United States alone who sneeze, wheeze, itch, and feel utterly wretched because of inhalant allergies at least a part of each year.

A weed of the genus *Ambrosia*, called ragweed, sometimes bitterweed, is the cause of a good portion of the torture in this country. Some people are living Geiger counters for it. While most of us do

not know it when we see it, others could detect the weed blind-
folded during pollination. When they come near the plant, they
immediately start itching and sneezing. The legions who are allergic
to its pollen do not suffer alone; all of us must help bear the expense of the estimated twenty-five million work days lost each
year because of this one weed. From mid-August to the first frost
its pollination is in full swing, and few areas escape its rain of
pollen. The heavily wooded areas of northern Michigan, Minnesota, New Hampshire, and Maine are nearly free of it. It is not too
prevalent west of the Cascade Mountains of Oregon and Washington, in the central Adirondacks, or in southern Florida. Elsewhere
the content of the air varies widely from day to day as the weather
changes. There is usually less pollen in a city than in the country
because there is less space in which the weed can grow. On windy
days the air's content of pollen goes up, but when it rains the air
is washed nearly free.

Surveys have been made under the auspices of the American
Academy of Allergy which show the relative standing of various
communities with regard to pollen. Chicago has an average in-
season count of 5780 pollen grains per cubic yard of air; St. Louis,
13,500; Nashville, Tennessee, 6800; and Dallas, Texas, an incredible
20,300. In contrast, Los Angeles registers only 85 grains per cubic
yard; Miami Beach, 194; the Grand Canyon in Arizona, 20; and
Alaska, almost none.

In Europe, where the greater population density does not permit
land to lie idle, ragweed pollen is not a problem. There susceptible
persons suffer most during the haying season, when pollens of the
various grasses are scattered about. In fact, the common term applied to pollen sensitivity, hay fever, was first used in England in
1812 when a physician noted the disease and connected it to the
haying operation. The name has stuck, even though fever is usually
not one of the symptoms and the disease certainly is not due to
hay alone.

In the spring, hay fever is usually associated with pollens of such
trees as the poplar, elm, birch, maple, and oak. It can also come

from grass pollens. Enough people are sensitive to rose pollens that a special name, rose fever, is sometimes employed. Ordinary house dust, however, causes many unfortunate persons to suffer year after year from sniffles that may seem to be recurring common colds. They have unexplained coughs; red, watery eyes; swollen neck glands; mysterious stomach and intestinal upsets; and headaches. Children who play with fuzzy Teddy bears, bunny rabbits, or rag toys that accumulate dust often are victims of house-dust allergies. Feather pillows or that old day bed on which one takes a nap may be the source of headaches, a fatigued feeling, and sniffles. Dogs and cats spread from their fur and skin particles to which some people are allergic.

Closely related to pollens are spores. These tiny bodies are everywhere adrift in the air, even over the vast oceans. Though similar to pollens in general appearance, there are important differences. Spores are the primitive reproductive bodies of fungi, yeasts, and molds. They are not exactly seeds, but they serve the same purpose. The fungus family, as we shall refer to molds, yeasts, and fungi collectively, is made up of minute members of the plant world, all of which we might call cousins of the mushrooms. There is an almost infinite variety of fungi, 100,000 being a very conservative estimate. They are in lake, stream, and sea water. They inhabit the soil. Their spores have been found in the air at a height of nearly seven miles; they occur over all the oceans. Spores and pollen grains are diversely represented in the arctic and antarctic atmospheres, being carried there by air currents.

The function of fungi is simple and essential. In nature, they cause rot and decay, thereby reducing all kinds of matter to simple chemicals that new vegetation needs to grow and flourish. Without them, all life would eventually come to a halt, for there would be no decay to transform old matter into new food supplies. Unhappily, not all fungi feed on dead material; a few prefer living plants and animals. Some varieties attack corn, some cereals, some fruit trees. Like cancer in humans, they drain away the plant's energy, which otherwise would be going into useful grains and fruits. Their cost to agriculture is terrific, but man himself is not entirely immune. Such common disorders as ringworm and athlete's foot are due to fungi from spores growing on the skin, and rheumatoid arthritis seems to be linked to a fungus disease of the foot. Spore-produced ailments of the respiratory system are rare—fortunately, for there is little medical treatment for them save rest. In this country one of the most prevalent fungus-produced respiratory ills carries the jaw-breaking name coccidiodomycosis, though it is sometimes called valley, desert, or San Joaquin fever. It is caused by a fungus that ordinarily lies dormant in sandy desert soil. Dust storms commonly spread the organism about, and it becomes active when inhaled, setting up housekeeping in lung tissue. Tornadoes in the Middle West also seem to be potent spreaders of fungus ailments because they stir the topsoil and pull old wooden buildings apart, both places where fungi thrive.

Although most fungi depend on the wind for dissemination, some species are provided with special and unique mechanisms for launching their spores. One mold shoots into the air a tiny pellet that bursts, discharging spores like sparks from a skyrocket. Another ejects spores in rapid succession like a machine gun. Still others loose a broadside of millions of spores which is so dense that it looks like a puff of smoke. The ejection may range from a fraction of an inch to as much as six feet. Once air-borne, spores are carried easily by the slightest air currents.

Spores are also remarkably hardy; many can retain their viability for years despite extreme vicissitudes of humidity, temperature, and sunlight. Their rate of reproduction under favorable conditions is fantastic. Whereas a pollen grain arriving at its intended destination can help produce at most one seed, a spore can increase its kind many times. A single spore of the wheat stem rust fungus may land on any of the some two million stalks on any one of millions of acres and start an infection, resulting within a week or ten days in the production of 100,000 or more spores like itself. Corn smut is one of the most prolific molds in the plant kingdom. A single spore of this smut can result in a large gall of twenty to forty cubic inches on a cornstalk in two weeks, and every cubic inch contains about six billion spores, each of which can produce another generation in two weeks under ideal conditions. According to estimates, one acre of corn with 10 per cent of the plants infected can produce fifty trillion spores; and this is a conservative estimate, for 20 per cent infection is not uncommon. Spore discharge in some fungi continues from May to September.

The numbers of spores in the air at times is incalculable. Clouds of spores of wheat and oat rusts rise from the threshing operation during epidemic years. In the Midwest these have been trapped as falling at the rate of nearly a million per square foot in twenty-four hours. At all times, however, spores of one sort or another are present in the air. One has only to leave a jelly jar uncapped for a short while to find it covered with a mold a week later. Wet clothes left a few days will almost certainly mildew, again from air-borne fungus spores. The molds we see on stale bread, shoe leather, and even plaster arrived through the air. Any fruit juice exposed to the air will ferment because of yeasts that reach it.

Long-distance dissemination added to their great abundance and ability to survive makes controlling spore-carried plant diseases extremely difficult. The Canadian wheat crop may be infected from the United States or northern Mexico by spores traveling with the wind more than a thousand miles in the short space of two days. New Zealand grains often suffer the same infection at nearly the same time as those in Australia, apparently from spores blown a thousand miles across the Tasman Sea. Spores causing the white pine blister rust have been found more than a hundred miles beyond the limit of white pine growth. A particularly illustrative mold spore shower, which shows just how widespread the distribution can be, was recorded on October 6 and 7, 1937. On these two days, Weather Bureau records show that air masses at elevations of two to six thousand feet moved rapidly southeastward and eastward, covering the distance from Minnesota to the Atlantic seaboard in about fifty-five hours. Thousands of tons of spores from the mold called *Alternaria* were picked up and carried along by this wind. Probably rising somewhere in southern Minnesota, greatly increased numbers of spores were first found in Minneapolis on the morning of October 6. By the next morning, stations as far east as New York City and as far south as Oklahoma City were recording the effect. During the day and following night the shower of spores reached Dallas, Memphis, Nashville, Atlanta, Washington, D.C., and New Orleans, many of these localities experiencing hundredfold increases in this particular spore.

Mountain ranges sharply decrease the interchange of spores and pollens. The difficulties that pollens encounter in crossing from one mountain valley to another are made use of by geneticists to keep flower varieties pure. Fertile valleys separated by high mountains, more than her climate, permit California to grow 90 per cent of the world's flower seed. The wheat fields of British Columbia and Alberta, being separated by the Rocky Mountains, apparently suffer little spore or pollen exchange. Apparently also there is little exchange between northern and southern Mexico. There is virtually no information regarding wind transfer of spores and pollens across the equatorial zone, but, from our knowledge of wind movements, it would seem rather inconsequential.

In spite of the number predominance of dust particles and the hardihood of spores, greatest peril for us comes from air-borne microorganisms—bacteria, the lowest form of plant life, and protozoa, the lowest form of life classed in the animal kingdom. Careful scientific studies over the past two or three decades have shown that the most prevalent and damaging infections to which man is heir can be and are spread through the atmosphere. This is not to imply that air is the most important medium of transfer. It is not; air is just one of several. Water, food, and direct contact are quite effective for most microorganisms.

The importance of air transmission, however, is just now being fully appreciated after having fluctuated back and forth over the centuries. The sources of epidemics were thought by ancient peoples to be the "winds." Attention shifted to actual contact with the sick during the plagues of the Middle Ages. In the nineteenth century, as the chemistry of gases came to the fore, attention turned once again to gaseous exhalations. A century ago, water was found to transmit intestinal infection, and then, a half-century later, insects were apprehended trafficking in blood infection. Thus microorganisms were established as the villains, but the air as a vehicle in the spread of diseases was most often disregarded.

A generation of physicians was taught that germ-carrying droplets ejected when the sick talked, sneezed, or coughed plummeted to the floor within an arm's length like grains of sand, there to lie and die. Now this comforting doctrine is shattered; germ-laden air is recognized to be an even greater source of contagion than personal contact for many diseases. These droplets actually evaporate almost immediately, leaving whatever tiny germs they contain to drift through the air.

Like spores, a relatively small fraction of the microorganisms found in the air can cause diseases in man, and of those that are capable of producing sickness, few actually succeed, for man normally has a high immunity to them. In fact, most bacteria are actually servants. Some, for example, convert atmospheric nitrogen to usable plant food. Pathogenic or disease-producing microorganisms, however, can be insidious adversaries. They propagate by subdivision—that is, each living cell can split into two other cells every thirty minutes or so. Each of the new cells then grows and divides again into two more cells. Provided with ideal conditions, populations thus double each half-hour. Such a fantastic rate of multiplication means that, unchecked, the progeny of a single bacterium would fill a space equal to all the seas of the earth in five days. Nature has obviously set up checks to prevent any such development.

Fortunately, air is not a medium in which microorganisms thrive. Unless the humidity is just right, most desiccate and die. Short exposure to the ultraviolet radiations of the sun kills them. Low temperatures greatly decrease their activity, and elevated temperatures destroy them rapidly. Yet, as in rat-exterminating campaigns —excepting the fabled exploit of the Pied Piper of Hamelin—a few usually survive. Under most favorable conditions some germs can live for months attached to rugs, clothing, or other objects and become again capable of infection if dislodged into the air. Bacteria are expelled by talking as well as by sneezing and coughing, and it has been quite definitely shown that some may then pass through the air and lodge in the mouth and nose of another individual. Sneezing, as might be expected, is the greatest spreader of microorganisms. Unstifled, a single sneeze can discharge more than twenty thousand organisms from both the mouth and nose.

There is no escaping microorganisms, although country air is relatively free of them, and in forests their presence is usually hard to prove. The leaves of trees and plants apparently act as effective filters. Ocean air becomes more and more germ-free the farther one goes out from the coast. As might be expected, germs are most numerous in the air of towns and cities, but even here living organisms are less numerous than might be expected, drying and sunlight rapidly decimating their ranks. In enclosures where large numbers of people gather and tight spaces like automobiles and telephone booths, most organisms are found. One study showed schoolrooms to contain twenty-one bacteria in each cubic foot of air, a subway more than twelve, an auditorium about eight, while the streets showed less than two.

Smaller even than bacteria are viruses. These entities, bridging the gap between what can be called living matter and lifeless chemical substances, range between about three-tenths and one one-hundredth of a micron across. Under high magnification they look like fuzzy golf balls, pieces of string, or even pencil lead. Those infecting man or animals are roughly spherical, but plant viruses seem to be characteristically elongated. Viruses are the cause of many of our most dreaded diseases: smallpox, yellow fever, typhus, infantile paralysis, to name only a few. Generally these ills are transmitted by ticks, mites, fleas, mosquitoes, and other insects, but the common cold, other respiratory infections, and perhaps polio are spread through the air by sneezing and coughing, much as bacteria-caused ailments are spread. An influenza virus particle, like a microorganism, can lie around on the floor for months and still be able to cause disease.

Insects of many kinds populate the air, bees, flies, and gnats being quite common, as every picnicker knows. These, because they are relatively large and strongly built, are able to control their flight except under extremely high winds or convection currents. Accordingly they are seldom found far above the earth's surface. On the other hand, weak fliers and those with large wings relative to their size, such as midges, aphids, and psyllids, have been found up to fourteen thousand feet and hundreds of miles off shore. Likewise, wingless forms of insects like ants, mites, and even spiders are sometimes found at great heights.

The fact that the upper air abounds with insect life of almost every description has important consequences. Though every port of entry is carefully guarded and interstate traffic is regularly policed, the movement of insects in the free air cannot be restricted or regulated. Because of the distances involved, chances of dangerous pests coming to us from across the Atlantic and Pacific Oceans probably are small. From the West Indies, Central America, and Mexico, however, insect pests may come through flight or by drifting with the wind at almost any time.

The world's worst cotton pest, the pink bollworm moth, seems to be a continuing air-borne invader of United States cotton fields. In spite of constant and apparently successful attempts to eradicate the pest, it reappears in southern Florida with frustrating regularity. A clue to its persistence recently came to light with the discovery of infected cotton plants growing wild in the Bahama Islands. These plants fruit most heavily from January to April, and the bollworm moth is found in greatest numbers during this season. This is also the season when most pink bollworms appear in Florida. At least one-third of Florida's winds in the period blow from the direction of the Bahamas.

In addition to large numbers of insects, there are enormous quantities of insect particles in the air. Pinworm eggs, for example, are lighter than air and float about easily. Scales from butterflies, moths, caddis flies, May flies, houseflies, weevils, and beetles cause allergic reactions and asthma attacks in certain individuals. Others can't come near bees; some are made sick by gnats. In the Clear Lake region of California, a gnat that appears in great numbers is particularly annoying. As an indication of the population density these insects can attain, a single light trap in one location caught, in one and one-half hours, eighty-eight and one-half pounds of gnats, or approximately eighty-eight million of them—and this was, unhappily, a very small fraction of the total.

As the earth wends her way through her orbit about the sun, certainly some of this cloak of vermin is left behind, much as smoke from the locomotive lingers after a train has passed. It is not inconceivable that a hardy spore is occasionally lost, to be picked up by another planet after aimlessly wandering through the universe; nor can one say for certain that, during the long ages through which the earth has passed, another spore did not find its way here to become the progenitor of some of the life we know.

8 pageantry of the sky

*It is remarkable how few people seem
to derive any pleasure from the beauty
of the sky.*

JOHN LUBBOCK, LORD AVEBURY

OF ALL sights to behold, the sky is unsurpassed in beauty, scope, or
grandeur. With endless majesty, a technicolor panorama is spread
throughout the atmosphere above us. A golden glow in the east
announces the dawn; a crimson western sky bids the day adieu.
The cloudless daytime sky is a gossamer canopy of blue. The
starry splendor of the night is more magnificent still when the
aurora weaves a delicate tapestry of color high in the air. Hardly
a day goes by without a parade across the sky of frilly, fleecy
clouds in needlework designs; or of white pillar clouds surrounded
by straggling cloudlets, like children about their parents; or of
dark, somber rain clouds, from which may burst a rainbow with its
regal array of colors. Upon occasion the sun wears a golden ring,
and the moon displays a multicolored cross centered upon itself.
The sun may, for variety, turn green or be accompanied by com-

panion suns. In its most capricious moods, the sky may seem to be populated by phantom lights, by inverted ships that navigate among the clouds instead of the waves, or by mountain peaks without visible means of support.

A vast azure dome is the sky's most magnificent feature, but it is not merely the nature of the atmosphere to be blue, as was thought long ago. Leonardo da Vinci suggested that the sky's color resulted from mixing daytime white light and the black of space, but white and black mix to give gray. It is not the true color of some ingredient of the air, like ozone, as was thought to be the case well into the nineteenth century. Nor is it due to light emitted by the atmosphere itself, for then it would appear blue at night. Were the air completely transparent or nonexistent, the sky would necessarily be black, a fact confirmed by our stratospheric bomber crews who fly above much of the atmosphere. Since it is not black to us on earth, the cause must lie in the behavior of sunlight when the substance of the atmosphere is encountered.

The sun's radiation is electromagnetic waves of many different wave lengths, the longer of which we feel as heat while the shorter we can detect by radio receivers. Our eyes are sensitive to a very small band of wave lengths near the center of the spectrum, a band we call visible light. Just as our ears distinguish between sounds of various wave lengths so that we hear tones as well as noise, our eyes differentiate between the wave lengths of light so that we see colors as well as brightness. The shorter parts of this visible band give us the sensation we recognize as the color violet, the longer ones, in increasing order of length, the colors indigo, blue, green, yellow, orange, and red. The colors of objects, from the deep red of the rose to the delicate violet of the orchid, are due to the wave lengths in the light in which we see the objects. If a rose is viewed in light which does not contain red wave lengths, it cannot appear red. For this same reason, fluorescent lighting sometimes gives a drab appearance to objects it illuminates. Fluorescent light, particularly from systems of a few years ago, is deficient in certain wave lengths of the visible spectrum.

If we liken light of different wave lengths to various-sized soldiers marching in formation, a fair approximation of light's behavior upon striking the atmosphere can be obtained. For our purposes we will have pygmy soldiers dressed in blue, ordinary-sized soldiers in yellow, and giant soldiers in red. They represent, of course, the respective wave lengths of visible light. If now these soldiers were marched over a rough, rock-strewn field, their size differences would certainly disrupt their formation. The giants would march on with little change in stride. The average-sized soldiers, though being slowed, would make it across the field with but few tripping. The pygmies, on the other hand, would stumble, fall, and be forced to detour around some of the largest boulders. If, from a distance, we could observe the field after most of the soldiers had passed, we would see only the blue-uniformed pygmies still struggling along.

Essentially, this is what happens to light when it encounters our miles-high atmosphere. The longer wave lengths plow through easily, but the shorter ones are scattered in all directions by the air molecules. They are not only deflected once; a few are bounced about again and again like a billiard ball after an energetic play. Therefore when we look overhead, except directly at the sun, we see primarily the shorter blue wave lengths, which are coming toward us from any and all directions.

Under clear conditions, the blue of the sky seems to descend between us and distant hills. This blue also comes from the air. Indeed, if the hills are forested and dark, most of the light comes from atmospheric scattering. The more distant the hills, the darker is the blue, for more air is involved. Unconsciously, perhaps, we employ this "depth of color" in estimating distance. Though no one has seen it yet, the earth will certainly have a bluish tint when viewed from outer space. It will look blue from above for the same reason the sky looks blue to us now from below.

Though generally blue, the sky may show any color, according to circumstance. Again, the color exhibited depends on the matter light encounters in the air. As we have seen previously, in addition to clouds, dust and all kinds of particle material are concentrated in the lower atmosphere. Being larger than air molecules, these scatter longer wave lengths of light. When the sun is directly overhead the effect is usually not important, for the light is approaching perpendicularly and must penetrate a minimum of dust-laden air. But when the sun is near the horizon its rays enter the atmosphere obliquely, passing through much more of the particle-laden lower air. All wave lengths are scattered; the blues are completely disrupted and only the longest red rays penetrate at all. The sky in the direction of the sun thus exhibits a crimson glow. The more dust or cloud particles in the air, the deeper is the color. Following volcanic eruptions, when great quantities of dust fill the air, the sun is particularly lurid and blood-colored at rising and setting. The red color is evident longer before sunset and after sunrise also. At times of particularly heavy dust concentration, a rust-colored light may be shed by the sun even at noon. If there were not always some dust particles and cloud droplets in the air to reflect sunlight, the sun would rise with dramatic suddenness and set with equal rapidity, those wonderful periods we know as dawn and twilight all but disappearing.

Dust also causes the intriguing phenomenon of the "sun drawing water." Despite the popular terminology, the true cause is sunbeams that find their way through rifts in the clouds and are rendered luminous by the dust in their paths. Less familiar but equally beautiful are crepuscular rays that, at twilight and occasionally at dawn, spread their stripes of shadow across the sky like a huge fan. Radiating from the position of the sun below the horizon, their origin is sunbeams breaking through clouds which may also be hidden beyond the horizon. When they are seen in the direction of the setting sun, corresponding rays are sometimes found converging toward the antisolar point in the east. Eastern and western rays are one and the same, individual rays that have run the entire celestial vault. Although they appear like huge arcs converging at their extremities, they are actually parallel, their arched shape being due to the same optical illusion that makes parallel railroad tracks appear to converge in the distance.

Luminous night clouds or noctilucent clouds are yet another twilight phenomenon caused by fine dust, probably of meteoric origin. For some unexplained reason, these have been seen only between latitudes 45 to 60 north and the same south. They are most frequent from the middle of May to the middle of August. Before sunset the sky seems perfectly clear. Then, some fifteen minutes after the sun disappears, luminous clouds begin to form into silver-white bands, changing into a golden-yellow near the horizon. For an hour or more thereafter they stand out brightly against the afterglow from the sun. Ordinary clouds, in contrast, are dark. Clearly the night clouds are still bathed in sunlight, so they must be quite high in the upper air. Generally this height is between fifty and sixty miles.

When the particles between us and the sun are small and nearly all of one size, certain colors can be preferentially produced. Smoke from great forest fires occasionally meets this size qualification, and gives the sun, appearing bland like a clouded moon, a blue or green appearance. Smoke from extensive Canadian fires drifted over Europe in 1950 (see Chapter 7), and a blue sun was seen for several days. A weather bureau or newspaper office will be swamped occasionally with excited telephone calls reporting that the sun or moon has turned green or some other peculiar color, surely a forecast of dire events. On the contrary, there is no cause for alarm; it shows merely that uniform-sized particles are drifting over at a height of some five miles. The phenomenon is not seen often, its rarity being attested to by the expression, "once in a blue moon." When first forming, clouds in the tropics have been noticed to appear blue even in contrast to the blue sky. The phenomenon is thought to be due to the very tiny droplets that make up the incipient clouds.

Tiny, regularly-shaped ice crystals floating high in the air produce still other effects. When, after a few days of bright winter weather, high clouds, feathery and fragile, give to the sky a milky white opalescence, bright rings, called halos [Plate 4], appear encircling the sun or moon. Halos of the moon are necessarily much fainter, and their colors are nearly imperceptible. But, sun or moon, the phenomenon cannot be called rare, despite the fact that a great many individuals profess never to have seen it. In many parts of the world, particularly the north temperate latitudes, halos are visible on the average as often as once each four days. Observant meteorologists have counted them on two hundred days during a year.

Clouds forming below freezing temperatures are made up of ice crystals or snowflakes. The simplest ice crystal, and one of the commonest also, is a tiny needlelike six-sided object. In clouds that are heavy and thick, these crystals tend to collect in clusters or clumps masking the symmetry of the crystals. But in thin veils of clouds, collisions are few, and single crystals can go their merry ways. They slowly flutter toward earth as a feather might, orienting their longest axis as nearly horizontal as possible.

A light beam striking such an ice crystal is partially reflected as it would be from a mirror. But, because the crystal is transparent, some of the light passes through it, and in so doing is reflected internally. This internally reflected or refracted light is given definite directions due to the symmetry of the crystal and is responsible for halos. The most intense refracted beam emerges after having undergone a direction change of about 22 degrees; another less intense beam, nearly 45 degrees; and other beams, still larger angles. Halos therefore appear at definite positions. The lesser-angle one is always the brighter; often it is the only one visible. Since red light is shifted somewhat less than blue light, the inner part of each halo tends to be red while the outermost part appears to be blue.

Flat snowflakes, another common crystal form, tend to present their broad sides to their direction of fall. Settling, they lie parallel to the ground, though they may slowly undulate like bits of paper wafted along by a gentle breeze. When the sun is low in the sky, mirrorlike reflection from either the upper or lower sides of such crystals produces one of the simplest of the sky's spectacles, a vertical pillar of light [Plate 4]. This apparition is best seen when the sun is behind a house or just over the horizon so that its direct light cannot dazzle the eye. Actually we see similar effects regularly, though they may not be recognized as such. A coarse pillar of light can be seen by looking at a street light through a window covered by a Venetian blind, its slats horizontal. The light reflecting from each slat, if a little imagination is employed, seems to form a vertical strip.

The sky's pillar of light is usually uncolored, that is, white, but when the sun is sufficiently low to become yellow, orange, or red itself, the pillar naturally assumes the same tint. If the snowflakes producing the effect are distant, the light pillar appears to hang against the sky, while a local curtain of flakes gives one seeming to be only a few hundred yards away. Pillars of light have been observed that were inclined as much as 20 degrees instead of being vertical. Here the ice crystals were not floating horizontally but were being carried along in a slanting direction by air currents.

Oscillation of the falling snowflakes, such as might be produced by a slight wind, sometimes results in a horizontal as well as a vertical strip of light. The two arms of light meet at the sun, giving an imposing spectacle, a cross suspended in the air. A feathery texture and a glowing, scintillating effect are added by the motion of the snowflakes, making the cross seem very brilliant and real. For obvious reasons a cross in the sky has had great significance since the time of Christ. Very probably such a celestial apparition induced Emperor Constantine the Great to acknowledge Christianity in the year 312 A.D. and to adopt the cross as his emblem. To see at any time a cross that is similar in all essential respects, we need only to look through a window screen at a distant light. The regular array of vertical and horizontal wires, instead of ice-crystal mirrors, is responsible in this latter instance.

On rare occasions more than one ice-crystal spectacle is visible at a time. Combination of the cross and halo produces an awesome sight, a four-spoked wheel in the air. Needlelike ice crystals form the halo, the rim of the wheel, while snowflakes fluttering down to earth produce the cross centered on the sun, giving the appearance of spokes. The wheel in the air that appeared to Ezekiel very probably originated in this fashion, for the Biblical text describes the vision as appearing after "a whirlwind came out of the north," which might be expected to bring flying snow.

Turbulence, or air currents moving first in one direction, then another, and occasionally standing still, can cause a multiplicity of spectacles. Several crosses at one time have been seen. In the complete absence of upper-air movement, ice crystals settling essentially flat with respect to the plane of the earth produce a halo that is parallel to the horizon. The extremities of the halo on either side of the sun then appear most luminous, and the sun seems to be accompanied by brilliant mock suns or sundogs, as they are more commonly called. Sometimes an ordinary halo circling the sun, a cross, and a mock sun appear simultaneously. Where the vertical arms of the cross intersect the halo, brighter patches of light are formed due to mutual light reinforcement. The sun then seems to be accompanied by four mock suns. The complete apparition, to which may be added still other incomplete arcs and crosses, is perhaps the most spectacular of all sights, and one indeed to frighten the ignorant and alarm the superstitious.

Clouds above freezing temperatures and fogs are composed of tiny water droplets which produce highly colored spectacles. When the droplets are a little less than one-half micron across, the light waves bend around them much as sea waves wash around a protruding rock. Where they meet behind the droplet they "interfere" with one another, giving a separation of colors. The result is a corona, a series of beautifully variegated rings of light about the light source, appearing like the aureole painted round the head or entire body of sacred personages. A softly radiant moon and even some of the brighter stars show coronas as thin, fleecy clouds glide slowly past.

Coronas may show several distinct concentric circles of color, each bluish on the inside, then passing through a yellowish white to a red-brown on the outside. Their diameters are only a few times greater than that of the light source. The largest coronas are formed by the smallest droplets, and the brightest colors are given when the droplets are most nearly uniform in size. A corona may be seen around an ordinary electric light bulb if viewed through a window fogged over with condensed moisture on a chill winter evening.

The most beautiful coronas are those around the sun, but they are seldom noticed because dark glasses or a mirror are required to block the sun's direct rays. When the stratosphere is loaded with dust, as after a volcanic eruption, huge coronas encircling the sun, called Bishop's rings after the Reverend Sereno, Bishop of Honolulu, may be seen under favorable conditions.

A cousin of the corona is the glory, a striking phenomenon commonly seen in mountainous country where the shadow of the observer can fall on a bank of fog. The watcher sees the shadow of his head, and his only, surrounded by colored rings. Quite naturally, the glory-encircled shadow has appealed strongly to human imagination. Backward scattering of light is responsible for the rings and also causes the effect to be visible only in a straight line joining the light and the shadow—in other words, at the position of the observer's head. The effect is rendered most uncanny because the shadow may be mistaken for another person seen dimly through the mist, the apparent distance creating the further illusion of gigantic size.

The most famous example of a glory is the "Specter of the Brocken." The Brocken is a granite-strewn mountain in northern Germany commanding a magnificent view in all directions. Because glories could frequently be seen there, the spot long ago gained a mystical significance in the folklore of the region. It is not the only place renowned for its glories, however. The Ben Macdhui region in Scotland is also well known, as is the Hawaiian crater of Haleakala on the island of Maui. To Mount Kumei in China have flocked tens of thousands of devout Buddhists to see the "Glory of Buddha." Some of the more fervent pilgrims, seeing their shadows in the center of a rainbowlike glory floating on the sea of white clouds below, have jumped off the precipice, believing themselves about to be received in the arms of Buddha and carried into Paradise. A pilot flying in sunlight above a cloud layer may see a system of colored rings around the shadow of his plane. Indeed, if the plane is passing through a cloud, a corona in front and a glory behind may be visible.

While the glory is familiar only to those who fly regularly and to the inhabitants of certain mountainous regions, an incomplete glory, the rainbow, is quite common. It is one of nature's happier spectacles, though it is not without the taint of superstition. Most of us have heard of the proverbial pot of gold (a gold watch to the Irish and a jug and spoon to the Norwegians) to be found at the rainbow's end. Some people still hold to the belief that a finger pointed at a rainbow will certainly be cut off or that the pointer will be struck by lightning. Southwestern Indian tribes once regarded rainbows as evil things that caused droughts by sucking up the water.

A rainbow is formed by light playing on water drops. Occasionally droplets of mist are the cause, but usually it is the larger raindrops. Fine cloud droplets can never produce a rainbow, nor can snowflakes. If a rainbow is reported during falling snow or when the sky is clear, it is certain that the snow is half-thawed or that a drizzle, such as sometimes occurs without perceptible cloud cover, is falling. The drops that produce the rainbow are usually one to one and a half miles away, although against a dark background such as a dense woods they may be seen only a few yards away. Indeed, a rainbow, as real as any, is formed in the spray from a lawn sprinkler or a fountain only a few feet away. A rainbow is not, however, at a fixed place like a real thing; it is only light coming from a certain direction. If we move, the rainbow moves. Every individual, though he may be standing in a group, sees a different rainbow; and, of course, the drops reflecting the light are falling so that each instant we ourselves see a rainbow formed by a new set of raindrops.

Light intercepting a raindrop is partially reflected and partially refracted as it is by an ice crystal. The drop, being spherical or approximately so, scatters some light in all directions, but a particularly strong beam, and one separated slightly according to color, is sent back in the direction from whence it came at an angle of about 42 degrees. A less intense though color-separated beam is also sent back at nearly 51 degrees. Light from the smaller angle forms the primary bow, and the larger the secondary bow, which sometimes is visible. When the sun is higher than 42 degrees no rainbow is possible, for the refracted light cannot be directed to us. For this reason rainbows are not seen from the ground in equatorial and temperate latitudes between midmorning and midafternoon. But as the sun descends toward the horizon, more of the rainbow becomes visible, until a semicircle is formed just as the sun sets.

Clouds themselves assume an infinite variety of shapes, all creations of art. Even the storm clouds of Chapter 5, despite their satanic fury, are majestic in their awfulness. The rarer cloud forms, however, are worthy of the finest sculptor. Regularly spaced bands with intervening strips of clear sky [Plate 5] are called billow, windrow, roll, or wave clouds. They form when a cloud layer rises into a layer of faster-moving air above, which throws the clouds into horizontal rolls. When a drier or warmer air layer suddenly drops into a cloud layer, a hole may be punched in the latter [Plate 5]. If the upper portion of a heavy thunderstorm cloud spreads out beyond the bounds of its rising air currents, it tends to sag, forming thereby a cloud variously called a sack cloud, a festoon cloud or, technically, by the rather descriptive name mammato cumulus [Plate 5].* A banner cloud floats like a great white flag on the leeward side of high mountains. Winds whipping over a mountain are calmed and reduced in pressure when they reach the lee side. Lowered pressure results in slightly lowered temperature,

---

* The exact physical process by which mammatus clouds (so called because of their mammary appearance) form is unknown, but a kind of reverse connection is involved. The effect is readily recognized in Plate 5 if the picture is turned top to bottom. Though observed occasionally in warm weather, seldom is the phenomenon seen as clearly as in this photograph. The clouds became visible around 6:00 P.M. and remained for nearly three-quarters of an hour. They covered an area some forty miles in diameter. Tornadoes, apparently born of the same general atmospheric disturbance, caused damage estimated at one and one half million dollars at Alexis, 50 miles to the west, during this time.

giving rise to this singular cloud that, though continuously evaporating, is constantly being reformed. Lenticular clouds also form over mountainous areas. As their name implies, they may be nearly round if seen from below, and fatter in the middle, tapering to a sharp edge like a magnifying lens if seen from a great distance off. They are merely ordinary clouds that have been forced into a streamlined shape by the rather strong air currents over the mountains. When the sun reflects off them, as it may near sunrise or sunset, they are apt to be rimmed with gold. Sometimes clouds are caught in a vortex and whirled into a circular pattern [Plate 4]. Even high aircraft leave a trail of vapor that condenses into streaks of clouds. Such formations are called contrails. From mountain peaks and tall buildings low-hanging clouds produce unusual scenes [Plate 5]. A storm cloud appears black from below simply because the quantity of water in it prevents the passage of sunlight. The same cloud viewed from above or from a side where sunlight is hitting it directly would look as white and fluffy as any cloud to be seen on a clear day.

Neither a cloud formation, a rainbow, a glory, nor any other atmospheric spectacle, except possibly a glorious sunset, can compare with the aurora—in the Northern Hemisphere the aurora borealis or northern lights, and in the Southern Hemisphere the aurora australis or southern lights. No written description or photographs can convey the true magnificence of these beautiful, ever-changing, luminous displays, often in vivid colors. Two nights in every three the region westward from Hudson Bay to Alaska, the Bering Sea, Scandinavia, Iceland, and back to Greenland is lighted by auroral magic, at its brightest sufficient to read by. During periods of intense activity, northern parts of the United States, central Europe, and Asia are included. When the southern parts of the United States, Greece, Italy, and Japan are favored, the display is usually very striking.

Not unnaturally, the Greeks and the Romans of earlier times regarded these northern lights with superstition, as portents of calamities to come. A band of light seen from Rome in early March, 44 B.C., was said to have foretold the death of Julius Caesar. Early

Norsemen saw the aurora as maidens, awful yet beautiful, who hovered over battlefields choosing those to be slain. American Indians thought them to be the glow of fires of northern medicine men stewing their captives.

Befitting the name, the northern dawn, given it over three centuries ago by the French philosopher Gassendi, the aurora borealis is most often seen as a glow on the northern horizon. Generally it flickers fitfully, suggesting a blazing fire just over the hill, the light from which is dancing among nearby treetops. Sometimes, however, the glow kindles into brilliance, assuming the shape of a huge arc; at other times it appears to hang in folds like a huge drapery. Often the arc bursts into feverish activity, some of it dividing into short rays, other parts into pulsating patches of diffuse light. Its prevailing yellow-white color becomes tinged with red and green. As the tempo increases, other rays leap upward, subside, then dart ahead again. The entire northern sky may become filled with gaily colored streamers and ribbons of light. At its greatest intensity, waves of light, apparently surging up from the horizon, fan weaker patches of light into new brightness, like a breeze blowing over dying embers. The recession is no less breath-taking. Often as suddenly as it developed, only a weak residual illumination is left in the northern sky, to be enlivened occasionally by weak, sporadic ray activity.

Auroral luminosity is caused by the entry into our atmosphere of tiny particles emitted from the sun. As explained previously, these approach the earth at speeds of hundreds, perhaps thousands, of miles per second, and are funneled into polar regions by the earth's magnetic field. The particles are electrically charged, for otherwise their paths would be unaffected by the field. Entry of these solar invaders excites the air molecules to luminosity between some six hundred miles and thirty-five miles up. Thus the aurora is not a reflection like a rainbow, and its apparent position does not depend on where the observer stands. Its light at any instant comes from that position in the atmosphere where the air is "flaming" into luminescence.

Other spectacles, also having no relation to raindrops, ice crystals, or dust particles, are to be seen in the air ocean. In many respects these are the most weird of all, though their cause is quite simple. Uneven heating of the air forces light rays to bend and distort so that tricks are played on our eyes.

A concrete highway exposed to the summer sun gets extremely hot, the air's temperature within a few inches of it rising many degrees above the average of the surroundings. The temperature of the air near a desert plain or over a grassy pasture can also become elevated as the sun beams down. A quiet lake may be warmer than the ambient air in the early morning because water cools much more slowly than air. The air layer very close to the water's surface is therefore warmer. On the other hand, the water also heats more slowly, so it and its contiguous air may be cooler than the surroundings in the afternoon. Likewise, a field of snow can make the lower layers of air much cooler than those a few feet above. These conditions make for mirages.

When the air adjacent to the earth is hotter than that immediately above and we look toward the horizon, our line of sight is bent upward as though a great mirror were lying on the ground. Instead of seeing objects near the ground, we are actually looking at the sky. The "puddle of water" appearing on a hot highway some distance away is perhaps the most familiar example. As we have discovered many times, the pavement is not wet. What we took to be water was nothing more than a reflection of the sky ahead. A hot layer of air just above the earth's surface can hide the base of a mountain on the horizon, while its upper peaks are clearly seen because we look above most of the heated air in seeing them. The effect is one making mountain tops appear to float in the air. Seafaring men pay careful attention to objects on the horizon and so are not easily misled. Men are not infallible nevertheless. Once Mediterranean sailors saw, with great excitement, what appeared to be a new island rising out of the sea between Malta and Sicily. Several set out to take possession of it, but, much to their chagrin, it turned out to be Mount Etna, whose summit, by a freak of refraction, they had mistaken for an island. Observers approaching the Great Salt Lake by train have watched, fascinated, the railway just passed over apparently sink beneath a shimmering surface of water.

A cold layer of air near the surface bends our line of sight down so that it tends to follow the curvature of the earth. Our vision is then extended beyond the normal horizon, but what we see is inverted just as an ordinary camera lens turns a picture upside down. The residents of Cape May, New Jersey, one morning a few years ago looked across Delaware Bay at Lewes, some thirteen miles away, to behold an odd sight. The town was inverted and hanging from the sky. It remained so, apparently, for fifteen minutes. In medieval Europe, where real castles were built on prominent locations and visible for miles, the spectacle must have been fairly common; it undoubtedly gave us the expression "castles in the air." The effects can be just as unbelievable over water. Passengers on the liner *Mauretania* once stood aghast as a passing cargo ship apparently heeled over, then split into two ships, one rising above the other. A steamer on Loch Ness in Scotland occasionally appears to leave the surface of the water and sail up into the sky.

Desert areas are famous for their vagaries of atmospheric refraction. In early morning, temperature conditions are often such that, even though the area is as flat as the proverbial pancake, a person gets the impression that he is standing at the bottom of a valley with higher ground all round. Later, as the sun rises and warms the ground, the opposite effect, one of being on a dry island surrounded by endless miles of water in every direction, is experienced.

Mirages afford an explanation of the Red Sea passage of the Children of Israel without invoking the miraculous but holding to the essentials of the biblical account. What looked like water to Moses' followers could easily have been a mirage, for the phenomenon is common enough on deserts with the sun shining brightly. Passing just north of the Red Sea, the Israelites may have thought themselves surrounded by broad sheets of water where actually there was none. As they advanced the watery plains receded; when they looked back, the Egyptian Army may first have appeared to be wading through water and then, as the mirage thickened, to disappear as if overwhelmed. The Egyptians, for their part, may have been fooled in the same way. Having seen their former slaves disappear into the mirage, they may have given them up for drowned and gone home.

Polar regions, even more than desert ones, are lands of fantasy and phantom. There are days when the sky is overcast with white clouds. The world is then one of complete whiteness: the snow-covered earth is white; the sky is white; even the air, though free of fog or haze, seems to be white in the diffuse illumination. The result is something that might be called the antithesis of darkness—absolute whiteness. There are no shadows; vision is, in effect, drowned in light. A man cannot see the snow underfoot; accordingly, he stumbles about as if drunk. He may talk to companions standing beside him and not be able to see them.

On other days, because of warmer and colder layers of air, the sun apparently rises or sets several times as its rays are bent and distorted. Sometimes the sun appears to be at two different elevations at the same time. In Antarctica wild mountain scenes sometimes loom on the sky line, beckoning exploration. Though they appear easily attainable in a few hours, they are actually far over the horizon and weeks of hiking away. In the middle of the Antarctic ice shelf a hundred miles from open water, topsy-turvy vessels with smoke pouring down from their funnels have been seen interspersed among the clouds. From about two miles away, an explorer's tent camp was once seen to swell into a pyramidal skyscraper city, and then, with a slight shift in wind direction, to disappear completely. Mystified, the observer dropped to his knees, and the camp reappeared. When he arose it disappeared from sight once more.

Not only light rays but radar beams as well are subject to atmospheric deflection, and many are the radar operators who have been sadly fooled by mirages. During World War II, when radar was a new development, there were numerous instances of warships battling phantoms. A cruiser in the Mediterranean bombarded a radar target without being able to sink it and without experiencing returned gunfire. Cautiously the cruiser bore down on the target, only to find an empty expanse of sea where a ship should have been. But, from the new position, another radar contact appeared on the same bearing as the original one and at approximately the same distance away. The second was the island of Malta; the first, which had been so thoroughly shelled, a reflection of the island.

Mirages are nearly as common high in the air as they are on the ground, though understandably only those whose business is meteorological optics are usually familiar with them. Small parcels of air of different temperatures and water vapor contents shift about continuously; these cause the stars to twinkle. Changing weather conditions and the shifting of air masses between night and daytime levels often cause stratification into varying temperature layers thousands of feet overhead. Though imperfect, such layers can act as a kind of lens to bring into focus a distant illuminated cloud against a background of darker clouds or to superimpose a dark cloud on a light background. They may transmit the lights of a city far beyond the horizon. They have been known even to reflect weird, zigzagging images of light that were nothing more than the headlights of an automobile winding up a mountainous road. In this day of expanding air travel, we can expect mirage effects to be noticed from higher levels with increasing frequency.

Mirages and other previously explained phenomena caused much of the furor of a few years past regarding the so-called "flying saucers." Though it is difficult to extract the facts and sufficient real information from the mass of material written and spoken when the excitement was at its peak between 1948 and 1952, it is clear—abundantly clear—that craft from other worlds or even other nations were not seen. Weather and experimental balloons, ordinary aircraft, and outright hoaxes account for many of the reported sightings. Searchlights, as used in promoting new shopping centers and similar enterprises, reflect from cloud layers to give the appearance of a brilliant object, now hovering, now darting back and forth. St. Elmo's fire and perhaps ball lightning, as described in a previous chapter, may have been responsible for still others.

The flying saucer epidemic began on June 24, 1947. A Boise, Idaho, businessman flying in his private plane near Mount Rainier spotted what he took to be a group of unfamiliar aircraft swerving in and out among the mountain peaks. Upon landing, he described them as being flat like a pie pan, so shiny that they reflected the sun like a mirror, and capable of great speeds. A few days later other Boise residents saw clinging to a cloud a disk that appeared bright and silvery. Though the mountain-skimming craft were very probably reflections from ice or snow-crystal haze wreathing the mountain summits and the mirrorlike object hanging in the sky was undoubtedly a mock sun, these incidents caught the public's fancy. Stimulated by newspaper headlines all over the country, they led eventually to a reaction of fantastic proportions.

In the next few months numerous other sightings were reported from both the air and the ground, but the initial craze was fading by the end of the year. Then an accident occurred on January 7, 1948, which brought the subject to the fore once again. Military and civilian observers at an air base near Fort Knox, Kentucky, saw something in the air that they described as an ice-cream cone capped with red. A flight of National Guard planes was directed to investigate, and, as they rose, the flight leader reported that a metallic something of tremendous size was ahead, and that he was going at least as high as twenty thousand feet before discontinuing the chase. That was the last report to the base tower; the plane vanished from the formation, to be found wrecked with the pilot dead the next day. Unfounded rumors that the pilot had been killed and the plane destroyed by the "thing" quickly spread. Actually, it was a useless tragedy. The pilot in all probability was chasing a mock sun, something as elusive as a rainbow. In his excitement he probably went to an altitude where a lack of oxygen caused him to lose consciousness and to crash to his death. The ground observers who started the phantom hunt most likely also saw a mock sun in conjunction with other incomplete halo phenomena.

A veritable rash of objects then appeared in the air, if all reports are to be believed. Magazines, newspapers, and even books were filled with speculations on interplanetary visitors. Even radar got into the act. Flying saucers were "detected" with these machines maneuvering over the nation's capitol. Though jet planes screamed out to search the region, nothing was ever found. According to oft-repeated arguments, this merely confirmed the well-known aversion of the saucers to more direct intercourse. The truth is, of course, that radar beams are bent and reflected by the atmosphere as are light beams and can register mirages just as our eyes can.

Flying saucers were simply the result of a widespread phantasmagoria kindled by revelation of the almost fantastic scientific feats of World War II and aided by an obvious tendency of the human mind to exaggerate oddities and wonders. Exaggeration is especially easy where atmospheric apparitions are concerned, for the limitless expanse of sky has no points of reference, no bounds or signposts by which to relate distance or speed.

Airplane pilots, whose reports regarding flying saucers were given great credence, are susceptible like the rest of us. Of course they are familiar with cloud formations and many other meteorological phenomena. They are nevertheless enclosed at night in a cabin lighted only by the faint glow of their plane's instruments. To their dark-adapted eyes, reflections off their cabin windows or off thin clouds can appear like brilliantly lighted objects. A vivid report, in fact, which gave flying saucers great impetus, very probably came about because of just these latter conditions.

Two airline pilots flying over Alabama in the wee hours of the morning in July, 1948, reportedly saw a wingless craft a hundred feet long with a row of lighted windows and an orange-colored exhaust flying beside them. They veered course and the object followed, then disappeared in the clouds above. Except for a few scattered clouds, the night was bright and moonlit. The plane's shiny aluminum body and reflecting plastic windows could easily have provided ample illumination to cast a reflection on adjacent incipient clouds. The plane's own red-hot exhaust pipes could easily have formed the orange glow radiating from the reflection.

This latest flying-object fever was by no means the first. It is almost certainly not the last, for there are a great many more reflections, mirages, and odd-shaped clouds to be seen in the sky than we realize. Ordinarily they are missed because most of us never really look at the sky. When some especially fascinating and weird report is published by a newspaper, everybody closely scans the sky for a few days. Quite naturally, other peculiar sights are seen, and a rash of strange "objects" is the result. Nearly sixty years ago, for example, inhabitants of Oakland, California, spotted a winged "cigar" flying above them. According to witnesses, it projected a stream of light and moved easterly at the great speed (for that day) of twenty miles an hour. In succeeding months similar objects were reported over Salt Lake City, then Denver, Omaha, and Kansas City. Earlier, on November 17, 1882, one of the greatest flying phantoms of modern times sped across the sky. This apparition was seen from many places by many people, including distinguished scientists of the day. The Oakland "cigar" was probably a cloud, perhaps a lenticular cloud, or a mirage; the earlier one probably was associated with an auroral display, for high magnetic activity was recorded at the time.

One can find a great many other accounts of mysterious objects flitting about in the sky. Strange lights appearing off the coast of England where treacherous shoals abounded in the early 1860's lured many ships to destruction. No one could solve the mystery at the time, but we now suspect that mirages were responsible. The residents of Constantinople were astounded on November 1, 1886, by a highly luminous oval body, several times larger than the moon, which floated in the sky. Two bodies like "two balloons of light tied to one another" were seen in 1863 and again in 1898 over Europe. The French scientific literature of the nineteenth century contains references to displays popularly called the "flying gas jet," the descriptions of which suggest them to be quite analogous to our most recent phantoms. Still earlier, in both the fifteenth and sixteenth centuries, strange lights aroused the populace of the west coast of Wales. And, as already mentioned, Ezekiel's wheel was one of the earliest and best-described apparitions.

However uncomplimentary it may seem, it is a fact that what we see is greatly influenced by what we expect to see. If it were otherwise, flying saucers could not have attained prominence and sleight-of-hand magicians could not secure a livelihood. It is also a fact that we notice mostly the things with which we are familiar. For all of us it is difficult to see new things, even when they are before our very eyes. If, knowing what to see, one would more often lift his eyes skyward, the reward would be some of the most remarkable wonders in the whole of nature.

9 wonderful waves

A thousand trills and quivering sounds
In airy circles o'er us fly,
Till, wafted by a gentle breeze,
They faint and languish by degrees,
And at a distance die.

JOSEPH ADDISON

LIVING IN an ocean of air, we cannot move without stirring it. We cannot open a door, play a piano, dive a jet plane, shake fruit from a tree, or cause anything else to move, without also shaking the all-engulfing air. Once we have done so, an air-borne quiver spreads outward in all directions. As a result, many quivers, each going a different way, continuously wash back and forth about us. They do so independently of one another, as if each were the only one in all the atmosphere. Most are quite feeble and run their course in a few hundred yards. They may, however, arise from terrific convulsions and spread completely around the world. As music, rhythmic air quivers have "charms to soothe the savage breast"; as noise, discordant tremors can drive a man insane.

We can see the blurred outline of a throbbing cello string. Touching our finger to a bell that has been struck, we can feel that it has been vibrating. From these motions we can readily see how airy quivers are born. At first air molecules close by are pushed violently away. Then they rush in to fill the vacant space left as the string or bell moves back, only to be pushed away again. Molecules farther away, being influenced by those first disturbed, follow this back-and-forth motion a fraction of a second later. Zones are thus created about the source of vibration where the air molecules are alternately more dense and relatively rare; or, in other words, where the air pressure is first comparatively high and then low. These zones fan outward as pressure waves to register as sounds upon our ears.

Sound is thus our usual perception of the rhythmic dance of the air's molecules. It is, moreover, both a sense impression and a disturbance of the air. Though we usually consider sound to be anything we hear, it can just as well be regarded as vibrations within the atmosphere (or water, iron, or earth, for that matter). In contrast to the definition of the listener who feels that sound exists only when it can be heard, the latter definition holds that sound comes from a vibrating body with or without anyone to listen. Whether sound occurs when a tree falls in a remote jungle is a question that can be answered either way depending on the definition chosen, but here we will adopt the scientific viewpoint that any vibration of the air, heard or unheard, is sound. So-called silent sounds and other atmospheric vibration phenomena can then be treated without the limitations imposed by the necessity for hearing.

Atmospheric pressure waves are much like the waves to be seen on a calm surface of water. Viewed from a lofty cliff or a high bridge, a bird diving for a fish excites a small wave system that expands in ever-widening circles. A passing boat forms a wedge-shaped wake of waves, which, advancing at regular intervals on the shore, rebound in different directions, cutting obliquely across other advancing waves. If the ocean is visible from our elevated perch, we can also see great waves rolling in from the far horizon, their crests here and there marked by white, foaming water. We then see trains of waves, great and small, wide and narrow, straight and curved, each gliding over the water as undisturbedly as if other agitations did not exist. Though it may appear that the water itself is moving toward the shore, it is actually performing only an up-and-down, back-and-forth motion, with no more of it flowing toward the shore than away. What is moving shoreward is energy, energy that in the case of ocean waves can batter down breakwaters, crumble granite cliffs, and wreck great ships.

Waves in the air are likewise really waves of energy, but for ordinary sounds the energy is incredibly small. The vibrating vocal cords of ten million persons carrying on normal conversations generate only about as much energy as used by an ordinary hundred-watt light bulb. Put another way, five thousand women talking on the telephone for one year would develop only enough energy to bring a gallon of water to a boil. We are able to detect such waves because our ears are extremely sensitive—so sensitive, in fact, that we are nearly able to listen in on the continuous rustle of the air's molecules clashing together. A person with average hearing ability can distinguish sound waves that would amount to pressure changes of only one hundred-millionth of an ounce on a square yard of area. He can do so, however, only if the pressure changes rapidly by this amount. Sounds are audible to us as a continuous tone when between twenty and twenty thousand waves per second are fleeting past. Young children hear the more shrill sounds—that is, the greater number of waves per second—better than adults.

Animals, particularly small mammals, hear still higher sounds. A dog, for example, perks up his ears and begins to bark when we have heard nothing. His ears are not necessarily better than ours; his are merely capable of detecting an atmospheric dance to which we are not attuned. We are, in a sense, all partially sound deaf, just as some persons are blind to one or more colors. Cats, small dogs, and guinea pigs detect at least as many as thirty thousand waves per second, while little brown bats, being even smaller than house mice, are sensitive to as high as a hundred thousand. At the other end of the scale is the deep rumble of thunder. Most of this sound is carried by waves no greater than one hundred per second. Much of it is, as a matter of fact, completely inaudible to us, being as low as two to five waves each second. We are sometimes made aware of these latter waves, however, by the rattling of windows and doors when the lightning is relatively near.

Since sound is a result of air-molecule motion, it cannot spread faster than the air's molecules move collectively. Under normal sea-level conditions the molecules are moving with an average velocity of about 1200 miles per hour; they are traveling in all directions, however. The resultant speed with which sound can travel turns out to be a little over one-half of this figure, or about 760 miles each hour. Being dependent upon the speed of the air particles, sound velocity is not constant. Decrease in air temperature at elevated altitudes or with weather changes decreases the speed with which sound travels. At 36,000 feet it is reduced from the 760 miles per hour at sea level to only 660 miles per hour because of the temperature difference. Altitude itself and decreasing atmospheric pressure in no way affect the speed of sound.

Knowing that sound travels with a definite velocity and that the pitch that our ears register depends on the number of sound waves reaching us in a given time, we can understand how, as is so often noticed, a change is heard in an automobile horn or a locomotive whistle as the vehicle passes rapidly by. When the listener and the source of sound are moving toward one another a greater number of sound waves are encountered in a second than would be were both standing still; the sound then seems to be higher-pitched. As the listener and the sound source move apart, the reverse occurs. Fewer sound waves are encountered in a given time, and the sound drops to a lower pitch. This phenomenon, known as the Doppler effect after its discoverer, Christian Doppler, was, oddly enough, propounded in 1842 to explain the colors of certain stars. For its original purpose the explanation is not now accepted, but it is of importance to sound and enormously useful in other studies of celestial objects (see Chapter 2).

Sound waves, like light waves, are readily reflected. If it were not so, we could not converse with one another unless directly facing. As it happens, however, almost any smooth surface is a better reflector of sound than the most perfectly silvered mirror is of light. The distances between the wave crests of audible sounds range from one-half inch to sixty feet; visible light, in comparison, measures only from one forty-thousandth to one eighty-thousandth of an inch. Since the effectiveness of reflecting surfaces depends on surface irregularities in relation to the length of the waves to be reflected, an acoustical reflector furrowed with deep grooves is better than an optical mirror having blemishes of microscopic dimensions. For the same reason small objects offer little obstruction to sound waves; the waves merely spread around, reunite on the other side, and pass on very much as if nothing had intervened. Just as a pole rising above the water's surface has little effect on the waves that roll by, a man standing on his lawn interferes but little with the sound waves that pass.

But a large obstruction like a rocky cliff or an eroded hillside returns an echo, as we well know. A sound suddenly produced and quickly ended, like the burst of a Fourth-of-July firecracker, may give multiple echoes when several reflecting objects are present. A sudden sound, if made a sufficient distance in front of a grandstand, will be reflected from the successive risers, and waves will return, one after the other, as a more or less definite note. Many localities are famous for their echoes. The deep chasms of the Grand Canyon of the Colorado River, by virtue of their precipitous and oftentimes parallel cliffs, give remarkable multiple echoes. Sounds from an alpine horn resounding from the rocks of the Wetterhorn or the Jungfrau gradually diminish by repeated reflections, giving the impression that the source of the sound is retreating farther and farther in the solitude of the Alps. The Gap of Donloe at Killarney reflects the sonorous waves of a trumpet for many round trips.

Certain reflecting surfaces may cause sound waves spreading out from one point to converge at another some distance away. Because of their domed construction, a number of famous buildings, among them the Mormon Tabernacle at Salt Lake City, St. Paul's Cathedral in London, the Church of St. John Lateran in Rome, the State House of Missouri, and the Capitol in Washington, D.C., focus sounds between certain definite points within their confines so that whispers can be heard much beyond the usual range of audibility. Such acoustical oddities are called whispering galleries. Perhaps the most famous of all is the Cathedral of Agrigentum in Sicily, where the slightest whisper is borne with nearly perfect distinctness between the great western floor and a point behind the high altar. By unlucky coincidence the latter position was chosen for the place of the confessional. Secrets never intended for public divulgence thus became known, to the great embarrassment of the confessors.

An ancient rock quarry outside the present city of Syracuse in Sicily is also a famous whispering gallery. This, along with its somewhat peculiar shape, long ago earned it the name "Ear of Dionysius." From the end of a passageway that leads to the ground above, one can hear what is said from nearly any point on the floor of the quarry. Tradition has it that the tyrant Dionysius, the great builder of ancient Syracuse, used such grottoes, and this one in particular, as prisons for his captives of war. Not only could his guards see everything that was done, they could hear every whispered word also.

Another striking sound-reflecting effect has often evoked the amazement of balloonists. While persons on the ground can be heard and understood plainly, the balloonist, in return, is unable to make himself understood. Though the phenomenon is due in part to the nearly utter silence, hence excellent hearing conditions, prevailing about the balloonist, the little reflecting surface in his case permits much of his voice energy to be lost. Earth-originating sounds, in contrast, are transmitted to him both directly and by reflection. Adding to the peculiarity of the situation, the balloonist can often hear the echo of his own voice and still be unable to arrest the attention of persons below. This echo is loudest over a still body of water and weakest over freshly fallen snow. It is weakest over unconsolidated snow because of sound absorption, or trapping, within the pores among the snow crystals. A similar absorption of sound accounts for the unusual quiet accompanying, and for a while following, a considerable fall of snow.

Sound waves, again like those of light, are refracted, or bent, by passage through air of nonuniform temperature. When the ground and the air immediately above it become hot on a summer day, sound waves skimming the earth move faster than those somewhat higher up, with the result that the entire wave front wheels upward. On a summer evening, the ground cooling rapidly cools the air adjacent to it more than that some distance above; sound waves accordingly turn downward instead of upward as before. This accounts for audibility at ground level being better on a summer evening than during the day.

The effect is more pronounced than one might expect, as proved by a somewhat undignified experiment of the famous English engineer of the last century, Professor Osborne Reynolds. Placing a ringing bell on a pedestal about one foot above the ground, the professor then wriggled full length along the ground away from the bell. At a distance of twenty yards he ceased to hear it. When he raised his head, however, the bell could be heard clearly again. At a distance of thirty yards the bell could not be heard three feet above the ground, and at seventy yards more than a six-foot elevation was required. Though thunder is a rather loud sound—estimated as great as two hundred million cornets playing at the same time—it is seldom heard at a distance of more than ten miles. Such a short range is a result of the sharp decrease in temperature with increasing elevation that accompanies thunderstorms. Updrafts and downdrafts that go with a thunderstorm work their havoc, for winds also bend sound waves.

A distant train whistle is more audible when the wind is blowing toward us than when it is blowing away, but the result is not due to the wind's driving the sound waves farther along toward us as one might first suspect. It is due rather to differences in wind velocity in the atmosphere, which turn those sound waves headed upward back toward the earth again. Because of trees, hills, houses, and other obstructions, wind near the earth is always impeded, hence its velocity increases with increasing height for some distance above the earth. When moving with the wind the higher parts of sound waves therefore move more rapidly than the lower parts and tend to be bent downward. But when traveling against the wind, they tend to turn upward and are lost insofar as listeners on earth are concerned.

Especially significant effects are produced by temperature and wind gradients where loud sounds are involved. On the occasion of the funeral of Queen Victoria in 1901, a battery of guns fired in London was heard in Scotland, but no sound was detected in a wide zone between. An explosion in Moscow in 1920 was heard within a thirty-mile radius and beyond ninety miles, but a wide ring of silence encircled the city. In 1931 sound waves from practice firing of the guns of our navy's Pacific fleet off Catalina Island jarred Los Angeles and broke windows in Bakersfield 150 miles away. Our recent atomic bomb tests in Nevada have shown the same hop-skip-and-jump characteristic and have revealed much about the behavior of waves in the air. They have, in fact, forced careful consideration to be made of air temperature, wind direction and velocity, and, to a minor extent, humidity before each test. Oddly enough, the location and extent of blast-wave damage, except at close range, is far more dependent upon meteorological conditions than on the size of the bomb.

Of course, at the site of an atomic explosion, air-pressure fluctuations as the waves go rolling by are of an entirely different order of magnitude from those we ordinarily regard as sound. A riveting hammer, usually thought of as giving a very loud noise, produces pressure changes up to one-half pound per square foot. One mile from an atomic-bomb burst at 2500 feet above the ground, the air pressure suddenly jumps to something like twenty-three pounds per square inch, then drops to twelve pounds, and finally returns to the normal fifteen pounds. As this blast wave moves out, it is influenced by conditions in both the lower and upper atmosphere.

The lower six miles of the atmosphere play the predominant role. Generally the air in this zone is cooler aloft than on the ground and tends to curve the shock wave harmlessly upward. Winds, however, if their velocities increase with elevation by as much as three miles per hour for each one thousand feet, overcome the normal temperature effect and drive the blast back toward the ground. In fact, in February, 1951, winds brought the waves from a Nevada atomic test shot rolling down upon the tiny settlement of Indian Springs twenty-five miles away. Dozens of windows in an auxiliary Air Force base there were broken, and an open door of a nearby ranch house was torn from its hinges.

Shock waves from another explosion of the same period struck Las Vegas, sixty-five miles away. Post-test examination showed that, in this case, wind and air temperatures contrived to focus the waves first at a spot in the desert eleven miles away where only prairie dog eardrums could be ruptured. The desert floor, being relatively smooth, acted as a very good mirror, bouncing the waves back into the air, only to hit again at distances of twenty-two, thirty-three, forty-four, fifty-five, and sixty-six miles. The sixth hop brought it to Las Vegas, where it cracked or shattered numerous large display windows in the downtown area. Though the test site was moved to another point eighty miles from Las Vegas, nature contrived for the city to be hit again. Two foci, one six and six-tenths miles and the other forty miles from the test shot, were created this time. Both waves hit Las Vegas, the longer one on the second bounce and the shorter on the twelfth.

Contrary to belief, around Las Vegas at least, blast waves are not reflected off clouds. The speed of sound through clouds differs only slightly from that through clear air, and shock waves pass through clouds almost as though they were not there.

The energy of blast waves that have traveled as far as Las Vegas is not great and poses no direct threat to human beings whatsoever. Pressure changes are no more than five pounds per square foot, or about that created by a forty-five-mile-an-hour wind. Store windows, however, are particularly vulnerable to such blast waves. Typical construction fortifies them against inward pressure with strong steel beams, but thin bronze frames hold most windows on the outside. The less-than-normal pressure phase of a blast wave therefore easily sucks them out.

Among the elaborate precautions taken to avoid even this damage to private property has been the explosion of an ordinary dynamite charge just prior to the atomic device's test. Through sensitive instruments placed at strategic points, the location of the main force of the atomic blast wave can be predicted and the test postponed if necessary. The surprising result of such studies has been that weather conditions can cause the blast force, as registered at a place like Indian Springs, to vary by as much as three thousand to one.

Lower atmospheric reflections rarely give focal points lying farther than 30 to 40 miles apart, and only then when severe winds are blowing. To explain jumps of 60 miles, as in the case of the 1920 Moscow explosion, we must look to the upper atmosphere. As we saw in an earlier chapter, a concentration of the gas ozone at an altitude of 10 to 20 miles absorbs certain sunlight wave lengths, warming the air. Another warm zone, the ionosphere E-layer, lies at about 60 miles. Both these zones bend sound waves, causing them to return to earth some 80 to 180 miles from the points of their origin.

Ionosphere-bent waves, so far as is known, never have been strong enough to cause damage. But those from the ozonosphere are a different story, the broken windows 150 miles away at Bakersfield, California, caused by the navy's guns being a case in point. Ozonosphere returns of atomic blast waves have caused minor damage at St. George and Cedar City, Utah, 130 and 150 miles from the test site in Nevada. A-bomb explosions are also heard more frequently at these locations than at Las Vegas, half as far away. Like all other waves, ozonosphere signals bounce and skip after striking the ground. On one occasion, thrice-reflected ozonosphere signals were heard in Albuquerque, New Mexico, 640 miles away, after an elapse of forty-eight minutes. On another, ozone-reflected waves bounced off the sands of the Mojave Desert and shook Los Angeles, causing an "earthquake" alarm. The Bikini tests of 1954 were detected with instruments half a world away in Germany eleven to twelve hours after the explosions. The most stupendous noise of which anything is known, the 1883 eruption of the volcano Krakatoa, which has been mentioned previously, was heard in the Philippines, Australia, Burma, and Ceylon, a maximum distance of nearly 3000 miles.

Throughout history human beings have been startled occasionally by the explosionlike sounds of meteorites crashing through the atmosphere. Infantrymen likewise have long noted the sharp report that accompanies a passing rifle bullet, and most of us have heard the sharp crack of the lion-trainer's whip. These sounds all have one thing in common; they are produced when, and only when, something moves faster than the speed of sound. In the case of an object moving at a comparatively low speed, sound waves push ahead, warning the air in front of the approaching object. The air, being forewarned, divides to make way. But as the object flies faster and faster, it begins catching up with its own sound waves and gives less and less warning of its arrival. When the speed of sound is reached, no warning at all is telegraphed ahead and the air has no time whatsoever to move aside. The object then is confronted with what amounts to a wall of air, which results in the creation of a sound, or pressure, wave much in the manner of snow piling up against a snowplow and water heaping up at the bow of a fast-moving ship. The creation of this pocket of air having no time to disperse gives rise to so-called shock waves, which are responsible for the sharp, cracking sounds.

With the coming of high-speed aircraft, shock waves took on new importance. In 1943 during diving tests of a plane called the Lightning, severe vibrations and violent jerking developed, giving a hint of shock-wave difficulties ahead for aircraft designers. Soon, still faster planes began going into uncontrollable maneuvers from which the pilot was unable to pull out. A fascinating story of aeronautical research and development then followed in the race for ever swifter planes, culminating eventually in craft that could safely break through this so-called "sound barrier" and travel faster than sound. With this accomplishment entered a new set of problems.

Beginning in January, 1951, a sporadic series of unexplained and widely scattered explosions occurred in the United States and Canada. Broken windows, shattered vases, and pictures knocked off walls were the usual reports. Supersonic planes then undergoing diving and speed tests were ultimately discovered to be the cause of the blasts. Below the speed of sound, both aerodynamic and mechanical noise energy is dispersed ahead of as well as behind the airplane; while above sound's speed, the noise energy lags behind. At just the speed of sound, however, the noise travels with the plane, accumulating sound or pressure energy all the while the speed of sound is maintained. Upon release, either by the plane's speeding or slowing, the wave of reinforced pressure energy spreads out, eventually striking the earth and causing what has become known as a "sonic boom." A boom is produced each time a plane reaches the speed of sound; if the plane attains supersonic speed, one is produced just as the speed of sound is reached and another as it drops back to subsonic speed.

The force of the sonic boom depends on the length of time the aircraft flies at just sound's velocity. It has been calculated that if sonic speed were maintained by an aircraft for thirty seconds, the blast would approach ordinary bomb force. The altitude at which sonic velocity is attained has a direct bearing on the force also. Not only is the atmosphere less dense at higher levels, but distance too exacts its toll on the energy wave. Sonic flight at an altitude of one-third of a mile produces a shock wave giving a force of about twelve pounds per square foot; at an elevation of 250 feet, however, the force is equivalent to fifty pounds per square foot, or about that of a 140-mile-an-hour hurricane wind. In fact, during low-altitude supersonic tests of a jet fighter in late 1953, the airport administration building at Palmdale, California, suffered cracked four-by-four wooden beams in addition to broken windows and door frames. Windows, doors, and door frames of other buildings in the Salton Sea area were damaged also during speed tests of the same plane. Once the cause was established, remedial steps were taken restricting supersonic speeds to altitudes above thirty thousand feet and, so far as possible, over sparsely populated areas.

Surprising as it may seem, much that has been learned about shock and sound waves has been accomplished by photographing them [Plate 6]. Since such waves actually consist of compressed and rarefied zones in the air and since light is unequally refracted by air of different densities, properly arranged cameras and lights can record the waves. A high-speed bullet gives rise to waves appearing much like those from a ship, including turbulent wake and bow waves. A model jet plane in a wind tunnel, through its wave pattern, reveals to specialists how its big brother will behave. Sound waves accompanying the firing of artillery pieces and the eruptions of volcanoes have repeatedly been seen, like hazy shadows, fleeting across the sky.

Though the idea seems to be widespread, it is not true that an eerie silence descends about the pilot when supersonic speeds are attained. If the pilot were in front of his plane and separated from it by even a short distance he could not hear it, of course. But being inside a cockpit that is an integral part of the aircraft, sound comes to him through the walls and enclosed air spaces. True, some of the sound is left behind, but plenty remains.

In normal flight a thousand-horsepower aircraft engine, either jet or piston type, converts about 1 per cent of its mechanical power, or ten horsepower, into sound energy. Recalling the minuteness of the energy of ordinary noises, ten horsepower represents great sound power, nearly as much, in fact, as all persons of the United States talking simultaneously. With individual engines reaching many thousands of horsepower and being installed in multiples of six and eight in a single plane, aircraft sound waves are becoming a problem of tremendous proportions. We will probably have to accept increased aircraft noise as an unavoidable consequence of progress. Noise-suppression measures can partially solve the problem on the ground; they cannot do so in the air. Already deep tones like distant, sustained thunder are to be heard many miles from research stations where giant rocket engines are chained, for the moment, to steel and concrete platforms undergoing tests. To calm their gigantic roar, mufflers as large as ordinary houses are employed. Obviously the muffler must be discarded during flight.

How to control and cope with the steadily rising clamor of all phases of our mechanized civilization is also a serious national problem. Noise now ranks with congestion and air pollution as a disadvantage of urban living. The last tabulation of noise complaints to police in New York City alone totaled nearly 300,000 a year. The din of plant and factory has, in the last ten years, resulted in deafness compensation claims of some two billion dollars. It has been estimated that business firms suffer a loss of four million dollars a day in over-all efficiency because of noise. Members of the armed forces, particularly Air Force ground crews, are severely hampered by excessive noises. On top of all this must be added the loss in frayed nerves and sleepless nights that millions of persons also endure, though the cost cannot be measured in dollars and cents.

Noise has very definite physiological effects upon us. Sudden or loud noises produce the same bodily reactions as a fight. Long exposure to high noise levels causes the bundle of nerves deep inside our inner ear to degenerate and to lose sensitivity much as the palm of one's hand becomes callused and insensitive after continued rough work. Constant noise to which we seem to grow accustomed nevertheless increases blood pressure and heart action and reduces our efficiency. When a large business office reduced noise 15 per cent, mistakes by machine operators dropped 52 per cent; absenteeism, 37 per cent, labor turnover, 48 per cent. When, in another case, an assembly operation was moved from a room adjoining a boiler shop to a quieter location, production increased from 80 to 110 units in the same period of time, and imperfections dropped from 60 to 7.

Turning from disturbing sound waves in the atmosphere to

sounds that are completely inaudible to us, we find phenomena fully as incredible as any audible sound effect. Probably the most remarkable is the use that bats, South American oil birds, rats, marmosets, and possibly other small creatures make of it. Ultrasonic sensitivity seems to be extremely well developed in the case of bats, those tiny "winged mice" we occasionally find in attics or dark caves. Even when totally blinded, these mammals can fly about in the darkness of a cave, dodging obstacles and hundreds of other bats. They do so by emitting an extremely short screech that, bouncing off obstacles, returns as an echo and enables them to guide their flight in much the manner of a radar-directed airplane.

The typical ultrasonic cry, really a click, of a bat lasts only about one five-hundredth of a second. At the normal speed of sound this means that the first sound waves are roughly two feet ahead of the bat's nose when the last wave leaves its mouth. If an object is three feet away an echo can then return in time to warn the bat of an impending collision. Bats, however, are observed to fly much closer than this to an obstacle before turning aside. They apparently solve this problem by continuously changing the sound of their cry and detecting a return from any part of it. The intensity of the bat's cry is as surprising as is its short duration and its modulation. A few inches in front of a bat's mouth, the sound pressure can be as much as ten times the noise of a subway train passing the station platform.

In keeping with his desire to control his environment in all its aspects, man is not overlooking sounds that are inaudible to him. These high-pitched vibrations hold promise for a number of unprecedented tasks, among them being the agglomeration of smoke and fog, the destruction of bacteria, the stimulation of plant growth, and the production of unusual heating effects. Though varying degrees of success have been achieved, small ultrasonic sirens have killed insects and rodents. Beekeepers have found sound capable of lulling bees into inactivity, so that their hives can be raided without fear of their stinging. The United States Navy and other organizations have experimented with large ultrasonic sirens to precipitate fog so that aircraft can land with a clear field of vision. The possibility of undesirable physiological reactions among bystanders makes the practicality of the latter application doubtful at the moment; for, although much has been written of the role of sound in causing neurosis and hearing impairment, much is yet to be learned of the effects of intense sounds independent of the auditory path. It is known, however, that relatively low levels of sound energy cause heating of furred rats and mice because of the absorption capacities of the air spaces between the hairs. Moderately intense sounds just above our normal hearing ability can cause skin burns, as well as bring death, to hairy animals. Even on hairless skin, rather intense yet inaudible sounds cause a systemic response similar to ordinary skin burn. Men going near the tail pipes of jet planes and thereby entering an intense field of both audible and inaudible sounds feel an acute burning where the fingers touch each other and on the ears and nose. They are seized with a combination of ailments that make the sight blurred, the knees weak, and the muscles painful. Particularly if the experience is a new one, men are likely to experience irrational fright. Very high frequency sounds produce changes in body cells that appear to be quite similar to those caused by exposure to intense radioactivity. In both cases the damaging effects are thought to be due primarily to a splitting of the water molecule into fragments known as free radicals, which in turn unite in various ways to produce hydrogen peroxide and other more or less poisonous combinations. Inside the cells these compounds cause nerve- and muscle-function failure and disrupt normal physiological processes. The victim, being incapable of hearing high frequency vibrations, may have no idea of the cause of his discomfort.

As a scientific tool, a technological aid, and a weapon of war, waves in the air have not been harnessed to their full potential. They can produce chemical reactions and extremely high air temperatures, drill holes, wash clothes, and accomplish many other useful tasks. The suggestion has even been made that, since the force and direction of shock waves are predictable, it should be possible to construct an aircraft having a large cross section for the express purpose of generating waves to be used as an alternative to guns, bombs, or rockets. Some work, particularly during World War II, was directed toward developing a gun to shoot not bullets but shock waves. Though one such gun was reported to have been able to kill rabbits at a considerable distance, its energy requirements were extremely high, making it impractical. But what the mind can conceive, men can usually accomplish. Only time will tell the future uses to which will be put the wonderful waves in the air.

10 the uncertain weather

> *Sometimes wind and sometimes rain,*
> *Then the sun comes back again;*
> *Sometimes rain and sometimes snow,*
> *Goodness, how we'd like to know*
> *Why the weather alters so.*
>
> CHILDREN'S SONG

THE WEATHER is an ever-playing drama before which we are a captive audience. With the lower atmosphere as the stage, air and water as the principal characters, and clouds for costumes, the weather's acts are presented continuously somewhere about the globe. The script is written by the sun; the production is directed by the earth's rotation; and, just as no theater scene is staged exactly the same way twice, each weather episode is played a little differently, each is marked with a bit of individuality.

The weather is many things. At some places it is a cycle of snow, ice, and gales; at others, wind-blown sand, rain, or sultry oppressiveness; in still other localities the weather is synonymous with season, one period composed of fairly consistent conditions being followed regularly by another. Prominent in the weather's compounding are storms, lightning, and wind, as described in previous chapters, but these features are definitely subplots in the everyday routine. Reduced to its essentials, weather is shifting and interacting air masses in which the forces of heat and cold, moisture and dryness are brought into play.

Though elementary, the idea that patches or pools of air with distinct properties could develop long remained obscure. The early Greeks divined that rain was somehow carried ready-made from the ocean and dumped directly on the earth below at the bidding of the gods, particularly Jupiter Pluvius. Yet they noticed that one could see clouds form, darken, and release torrents of rain. Some long-forgotten genius probably observed that water boiling in a cooking pot disappeared slowly and reappeared on the cold rock walls of his dwelling. Through realizing that water could be carried similarly from the ocean and later converted into rain over land, the rudiments of weather processes were guessed. But a thin film of water on a windowpane is a long way from a downpour. Until he was able to measure the air's temperature, test its pressure, note the wind direction, and gather such information simultaneously at many places, man was denied more than a cursory understanding of the weather. He was much like the three blind men, each of whom attempted to describe an elephant after independently feeling its tail, its leg, and its side.

When Benjamin Franklin discovered in 1747, through correspondence with his brother, that weather conditions sometimes drifted eastward from Philadelphia in the morning to New York at noon and Boston in the evening, he lifted slightly the veil of mystery surrounding the weather. But little use could be made of the information. A man attempting to ride even the fastest horse from city to city with a report of current weather would have found his information woefully out of date by the time it could be delivered.

The advent of the telegraph changed this situation, but, as is often the case, a drastic event was required to inspire action. More than any other, the sinking of French and British vessels engaged in the Crimean War by a violent storm on November 14, 1854, focused attention on the possibilities of the infant science of meteorology. At the instigation of the French War Ministry, this particular storm's path was retraced, and it was shown that the catastrophe might have been avoided had the newfangled telegraph been used to warn the ships. Storm-warning systems were subsequently set up in Europe and, later, in the United States. A means thus came into being for making scientific weather study a reality.

Even though there is still much to be learned about the weather as a world-wide entity, we know that basically it follows phenomena observed in everyday experiences as surely as a puppet the manipulations of his master. The fog that condenses on the bathroom mirror after we have had a hot shower is a cousin of a raincloud. When a bicycle pump becomes hot as air is forced from it, or when the sultry oppression of a summer day is relieved by a breeze blowing across one's sweat-soaked shirt, we are once again experiencing in miniature phenomena that shape the weather.

Unfortunately there is neither a beginning nor an end to weather processes; like the rim of a wheel, the weather moves round and round through endless cycles. We cannot, then, as admonished by the old saying, "begin at the beginning," but we must break in somewhere. Perhaps the most appropriate place to interrupt the chain of events is during the disappearing routine of the weather's magic show.

Just as sugar or salt dissolves invisibly in a glass of water, water itself disappears into the air. Under the influence of the sun's heat, water vapor is constantly rising into the atmosphere from rivers, tropic seas, fields, forests, and even polar ice and snow. Though invisible, water vapor is the agent that triggers the devious changes of the weather; it is the vivacious character that imparts suspense and intrigue into our weather melodrama.

When a water molecule breaks free of its parent ocean, lake, or roadside puddle, it takes with it a bit of the sun's radiant energy hidden in the electric forces that hold it together. In nature, energy is wealth, and like many an adventurer into a new realm, the water molecule is eventually induced to part with its wealth and thereby return to liquid water. The temptress who accomplishes the feat is none other than an air-borne mote, most likely a tiny salt crystal, itself originating from some salty sea spray. Gathering about these nuclei in the cooler levels of the atmosphere, instead of on a bathroom mirror as in our usual experience, water-vapor molecules become cloud droplets. In so doing they cash in their purloined wealth of energy that they may have managed to hang onto for, perhaps, three weeks. It may be that water vapor from the Gulf of Mexico expends its energy in a riotous thunderstorm over Chicago, or that vapor born of a languid South Atlantic Ocean returns to water in the stormy Strait of Magellan. At any rate, nature's books must always balance; energy and goods receivable are exactly equal to energy and goods payable. Nearly one billion tons of water vapor are produced each minute, and nearly one billion tons of rain fall upon the earth in the same time. Just producing this vapor amounts to a world-wide powerhouse operating at the fantastic capacity of nearly three million billion horsepower, with never a single raindrop escaping the accounting.

The air, though less spirited than water vapor, is by no means an altogether stolid fellow. When pressed it becomes hot; when relieved of pressure it expands and cools. In the atmosphere a rising parcel of air is subjected to less and less pressure; hence it becomes cooler as its elevation increases, and when forced back to earth it becomes hot again.

The magiclike winter chinook that sometimes sweeps across western Canada reveals in one neat package the important characteristics of water vapor and air. A moisture-laden body of air breaks from its lair over the northern Pacific and heads eastward, its temperature in the vicinity of 35 degrees Fahrenheit. As it rises to fifteen thousand feet to cross the Canadian Rockies, its temperature drops toward zero and its moisture is dumped as rain and snow on the westward mountain slopes. Had the air been dry when it left ocean levels, its temperature would have decreased to minus 40 degrees, or about 5.5 degrees Fahrenheit for each thousand feet of elevation gained, but because of the heat carried by the water vapor, its actual drop in temperature is only about half what it might have been. Upon descending the other side of the mountain, the air, now relieved of its water burden, is recompressed, and its temperature rises a full amount. The air becomes like the breath of spring, 50 or 60 degrees, and brings welcome though brief respite from the intense cold normal for the season. Not surprisingly, the chinook melts the snow as effectively as the fiery breath of a legendary dragon dispersed his enemies. It does so merely because a pressure decrease, occasioned by the scaling of the mountains, releases the heat entrapped in the water vapor. Nature can apparently pull a rabbit from a hat and yet be extremely simple.

In similar fashion, summer-afternoon showers arise from the changing fortunes of a single parcel of air. Lying still upon the land, the lower levels of air are heated from early morning by the warm rays of the sun. Moisture rises from steaming fields and forests. By midafternoon an entire area is overlain with warm, humid air, which is welling up with increasing rapidity into higher and cooler zones. As the air ascends, it is relieved of pressure and becomes still cooler. After a time some part of the ascending current reaches a level at which its water vapor begins condensing into visible clouds. Once this process starts, the heat energy extracted by the water when it became vapor is liberated within the cloud itself, serving further to raise the ever mounting currents. Now the point of no return is reached; a full-fledged thunderstorm will be born of the instability.

As in other cases of weather change, the first visible evidence of thunderstorm activity is to be found in the clouds. In this particular instance, the clouds are so characteristic that they might as well be billboards with neon lights. About lunchtime scattered cloud caps make an appearance. Rapidly they enlarge and boil up, while their lower parts unite to form a darker base. In the space of an hour or so the highest, rounded cloud tops begin to gleam and glisten, for they have now reached heights where ice crystals form even though we, sweltering at the earth's surface, find a snowstorm in sight hard to believe. We are shortly reminded, however, that all levels of air are intimately related, for surface winds sweep in to replace the rising air, lightning flashes, and curtains of rain—sometimes hail—descend on the earth below. In a very short time, maybe fifteen minutes, the storm weakens. Even before all the moisture is extracted from the air, violent disruptive forces upset the pattern that gave the storm its birth, and condensation ceases. The thunderstorm becomes like a ship without fuel. The seething, churning clouds halt their motions and fade away. A refreshed and invigorated world is greeted by the sun.

Occasionally hail falls from a thundercloud. For this to occur the updrafts become so swift that in some sections of the cloud the raindrops simply cannot fall. Instead, carried higher and higher, they are frozen by frigid upper-air temperatures, much as ice cubes are formed in a refrigerator. Collisions among the frozen drops and those yet unfrozen cause the ice stones to grow larger and larger, until gravity at last overcomes the lifting currents and descent is possible. Hailstone size is an indication of the fierce upward winds that can be involved. Golf-ball dimensions are not unusual, and even baseball and ostrich-egg sizes form. Crops are often damaged, and the giant hailstones sometimes destroy cattle. Every year human beings are injured, occasionally killed by hail. As many as nineteen persons are known to have lost their lives in one hailstorm, making credible the story in the Book of Joshua relating that of a Canaanite army more were killed by hailstones "than they whom the children of Israel slew with the sword."

The fog that appears on a cool clear night in low spots and disappears rapidly with the morning sun is but another chapter in the life of a pool of air. As night approaches and the wind ceases its stirring, the heaviest, coolest air drains downward as far it can go, collecting in hollows, over ponds, and along streams. The air is trapped and unable to sink farther, and such heat as it had slowly escapes. The air chills and some of its water vapor condenses into the droplets we recognize as fog. Other water vapor condenses as dew on grass and plants in the same way that our breath clouds a windowpane. If the temperature is sufficiently low the moisture is condensed as tiny ice crystals and a glistening frost is spread across the landscape. With the rising sun, heat is again acquired and the water returns to its vapor state.

The great fogs that roll in from the sea seem to arise in a different way, but actually cooling of a body of air is again the cause. Moist air from the Gulf of Mexico, for example, slowly and uniformly chills when it spreads over the cooler land that is Texas and the Southeast in the winter, its moisture thus becoming fog. Over the North Atlantic, warm air riding north with the Gulf Stream is gradually cooled as the southern waters mix with the cold Labrador Current, giving rise to the fogs of that area. Cold water welling up from the bottom of the Pacific along the west coast causes a narrow strip of water off shore to be considerably cooler than that a few miles out. The cool water area causes cooler air zones and hence fogs.

Most weather, however, is the child of conflicting air masses and not single parcels of air. Appropriately, this development in understanding the weather came from Scandinavia, the land of Norse mythology relating the wicked, never-ending struggle between Thor, god of lightning and summer heat, and Rime, the giant of frost and cold. Professor Vilhelm Bjerknes of Norway discovered about the time of World War I that enormous masses of cold, dry air irregularly sweeping out from polar regions exerted a tremendous influence on weather processes throughout the Northern Hemisphere. This discovery made world-wide weather development intelligible.

Over great sections of the earth's surface, air collects in relatively stagnant pools, which come in a few days' time to have a uniform temperature and moisture content, level for level. Air over the poles is relatively cold, while equatorial or tropical air is likely to be moist. In the sun-forsaken winter wastelands of northern Siberia, for example, a mass of air hundreds of miles in diameter can count on weeks of undisturbed repose. Seeping up the penetrating cold, the air's temperature drops toward 100 degrees below zero. Cooling, it contracts and sucks in air from outlying regions.

Thus this air mass starts as a region of lowered atmospheric pressure, but it grows denser as air flows in and presses ever heavier upon the land. Becoming eventually so gigantic and heavy that it can no longer maintain its balance on our whirling earth, the great mass of air breaks away and, probably influenced by upper-air currents, journeys far from its original homeland. On our own continent similar masses of cold air periodically develop over northwestern Canada and Alaska. Still another favorite nesting place for a weather-breeding mass of cold air is over the northwest Atlantic. These air masses too, after a protected childhood, begin to reach with icy fingers beyond their original bounds. The greatest single weather factory, one influencing events throughout much of the Southern Hemisphere, is the vast frozen Antarctic continent, where temperature differences of 100 degrees are not uncommon over distances no farther apart than New York and Chicago.

Cold air masses are not the only ones, however, that develop and whirl their way about the earth. Warm, moist air accumulates also, principally over subtropical waters. Here the added heat creates an expansion of the air and results in a high-pressure area. Unlike the state of things in polar regions, where a vacationing sun provides the necessary initial stability, uniformity of conditions in tropic areas is produced by the vast acres of water. Soaking up the daytime heat and meting it out at night, the seas change temperature ever so slowly. This stability works a soothing spell on the overriding air. In our part of the world, the Gulf of Mexico and that part of the Pacific below southern California cradle the warm air masses until accumulation and the revolving earth force them to move on.

Wise overseer that nature is, excesses—either in heat, cold, pressure, moisture, or dryness—are not long tolerated. Inevitably, displaced masses of cold air, moving under the inexorable forces created by our rotating planet, collide with warm, moist air. Collision occurs primarily in the earth's temperate zones. The United States, having no east-west mountain ranges to act as natural barriers, is unceasingly exposed to weather resulting from the jousting air masses.

In rhythm with the seasons, the meteorological conflict sways back and forth. During winter months, cold air masses, having grown to maturity in the Canadian wilds, sweep southeasterly across our Midwestern states as far as the very tip of Florida, driving back the forces of warm air. Six months later, pulsing masses of warm air from the Caribbean or the Gulf of Mexico hold the upper hand. By analogy with military terminology, the zone of conflict between two air masses is called a front. If the warm air is attaining supremacy, the meteorologist speaks of a warm front; if the cold air mass is carrying the field, he calls it a cold front.

Like armies, each air mass follows tried and true tactics and strategy as though prescribed by a battle manual. Their courses of action in subjugating an area or in conducting a retreat differ markedly, but in both cases the behavior is in keeping with their character. The one is cold and comparatively devoid of water vapor; moving ponderously, it suggests thick syrup. The other, resulting from an expanded mass of warmed air, is lighter and flows more freely; in addition, it carries a reserve of energy in its water vapor. Surprisingly, winds from the north and winds from the south do not intermingle freely. Each retains its individuality. The zone of conflict, the front, is sometimes nearly vertical and very narrow in comparison to the areas covered by the conflicting masses, so narrow in fact that it can be located by a single line on a map. At other times it slopes like a ramp, its foot anchored in a definite line along the earth's surface but with its upper reaches forging far ahead.

Cold air, being heavier, hugs the ground and tries to present a sloping or wedgelike battlement; cold air's tactic is to lift its adversary as would a charging bull with lowered horns, or in the manner of a snowplow. When the northern air is carrying the field, however, friction with the ground tends to blunt its attacking wedge, and the air immediately behind spills over somewhat like ocean breakers. A very narrow front is the result, one often outlined by brief rain squalls or tempests of snow followed by rapid clearing, a shift in wind direction, and of course colder weather. The cold front strikes usually with little warning. Along its forward wall are towering clouds, and, if the opposing warm air is sufficiently moist, thunder and lightning come even in the winter. When rain falls it is likely to consist of large drops like those of a summer thunderstorm. The tempestuous and gusty winds are treacherous, making a cold front hazardous for aviators and small-boat pilots.

A warm air mass achieves its conquest differently. Its attack is less spectacular and not as violent, but, incongruously, it can be quite destructive. Warm air, meeting the sloping wedge of cold air, has no choice but to rise and override the cold air, leaving control of the contested ground temporarily in possession of the cold air. Slow, steady rain or snow falls from the elevated air layer. Dropping through the exposed colder air below, the rain sometimes freezes during the descent, becoming window-rattling sleet. It may be well to point out here that raindrops cannot freeze into snow. Though snowflakes may melt into drops, the beautiful flakes of snow can form only from water vapor directly condensing without going through the liquid state. In wintertime conditions usually favor rain, snow, or sleet, but, if the lower air is chilled to precisely the right temperature, the cold rain will freeze just at ground level on trees and power lines. Fortunately, because freezing rain requires very specific temperature conditions, it usually does not last long. As the warm air brings in its reserve of heat energy, the cold gradually but stubbornly withdraws. The temperature rises slowly and usually in sufficient time to prevent great ice damage.

A warm front heralds its approach long in advance. Riding as much as a thousand miles ahead of the surface front, high, thin wisps of ice-crystal clouds, popularly called mares' tails, form from the first traces of water vapor pushing up and over the colder air. As the warmer air advances the cloud cover gradually thickens, and halos are to be seen about a veiled sun or moon. As the climbing air deepens still more, lower and heavier clouds develop and gentle rain begins to fall, increasing steadily to heavy rain. At last, when the warm front passes in its full depth, precipitation ceases, atmospheric pressure rises, clouds disappear, and a day or so of springlike weather may follow, even in midwinter.

Usually the clash of hot and cold air masses is not fought out by a head-on collision of the two. In such cases, a neutral air mass may be drawn into the fray, further complicating the picture. For example when cold Canadian air advances southward on a front between the Great Lakes and the Rockies and a warm front pushes northward east of the Mississippi, contact is established by a sort of glancing blow somewhere over the Mississippi Valley. The struggle is vigorously contested, nevertheless. Heavy rain or snow falls in the area of contact, and, as its substance is removed from the atmosphere, a deficiency of pressure is created. Other air must then move in to fill the partial vacuum. This the lighter, freer-flowing warm air does more easily than the heavier, thicker cold air. It flows inward, not on a gently sloping plane as previously described, but on a spiraling incline because of the twisting movement of the two simultaneously advancing fronts. The conflict leads to a gigantic whirling machine in the atmosphere, which gobbles up warm, moist air and spews out wind and swirling rain. It continues, moving eastward, as long as supplies of energy are received from the water vapor flowing with the air into it.

At the height of the paroxysm, the circling winds may pull in moist air lying over the Atlantic and gain renewed vigor. Now into the maelstrom blows cool, wet air from the east to infuse its character with the warmer air trying to move northward and the cold, dry air pushing southward and eastward. The eventual result is that the warm southern air is slowly but surely nudged out and its moisture-borne energy can no longer be brought to bear. The weather disturbance moves out to sea, where it fades away in the vicinity of Bermuda.

While this has been taking place, an offshoot of the original cold air mass is likely being challenged elsewhere. When the cold front moved south a part of it shouldered its way, perhaps, as far as Texas before grinding to a halt. This part was never involved in the battles to the east, but now warm air off the Gulf or from over the Rockies moves against it. Another in the endless sequences of fair and foul weather begins.

The eastern and western parts of our country regularly come

under the influence of still other air masses. In winter and early spring, cold and damp polar air from the north Atlantic blankets eastern Canada, occasionally to sweep in from the northeast upon New England. Warm, moist air beginning at sea off southern California moves westward across the Pacific, then turns to ride up the coast of Asia and back across the Pacific by a more north- erly route. Ultimately it moves inland along our northwest coast and sheds its much-traveled moisture in vast quantities on the coastal mountains or the Rockies. Later, relieved of moisture, it descends upon the southwestern plains states, warmed and dried. The same air that brings to one part of the nation a high annual rainfall thus helps make an arid region of another.

England, like the United States, is a meteorological arena. Struggling for mastery of her air spaces are cold masses from the vicinity of Iceland, warm air from the middle Atlantic, and air representing the varying conditions of the continent of Europe. The Mediterranean area, on the other hand, experiences a very regular sequence of atmospheric conditions, dry summers and capri- cious, stormy winters.

Because of its vast expanse, the Pacific Ocean influences a large part of the world's weather. In summer winds from the central Pacific blow inland over Asia from India to Korea, bringing rain in abundance to the rim of that continent. The Gobi Desert, hidden deep in the interior, gets only winds already squeezed dry. South- west Asia and North Africa, too, lie in the path of this already dried air. These regions are the driest and hottest found on the globe. In winter, polar air from Siberia pours down across Asia and diverts the Central Pacific air over the Indian Ocean and Aus- tralia. Being elevated and cooled, the warmer Pacific air is divested of much of its moisture over the East Indies, and it becomes rela- tively dry and hot by the time it descends on western Australia, again a desert area.

Much of South America's weather is dominated by warm tropical air blowing off the Atlantic across the great bulge that is Brazil. Tremendous amounts of water vapor are carried westward by it, feeding the world's largest river system, the Amazon. When at last the Andes are reached, the mass of air turns south, where it usually runs into another air mass coming north from the Argentine pampas.

The air-mass movements and fronts we have been considering are necessarily much simplified. Rarely do actual conditions fall exactly into the typical forms. Fronts of any kind, anywhere, may be so mild as scarcely to be recognizable. They may appear to fade for a time and then regenerate into very active disturbances. Two cold fronts may trap and elevate a warmer air mass so that the front dumps clouds and rain on mountain peaks yet is relatively unnoticed in the lower country between the peaks. One front may tread on the heels of another, badly confusing the conditions between them. It is such occurrences as these that complicate weather analysis and prediction.

Though the United States, Europe, and a few other parts of the world are laced with weather stations, much of the earth's day-to-day weather is virtually as unknown today as it was when Columbus sailed westward. Vast ocean areas are essentially blank on the weather map. Obviously, the forecaster starts with two strikes against him when he attempts to chart the weather a few days in advance.

Still, in this age of the hydrogen bomb, rocket missiles, and television, when polio is conquered by vaccine, when powerful germ-killing drugs have taken the fear from dread diseases, it is difficult to understand why predicting the weather a few days hence should present such problems. It must be remembered, however, that the atmosphere is one vast and inordinately complex domain. The over-all plan of grand atmospheric processes is not even certain at the present time. Currently two ways of looking at weather processes are being debated. One group of scientists holds that the fluid atmosphere conforms to definable hydrodynamic equations of motions, and hence the weather situation at a particular time determines its course for some period into the future. The other group, and presently the one in the minority, sees the weather as being always on the verge of instability, like a pencil balanced on its point. This second school of thought thus maintains that the weather is essentially probabilistic and that the best forecast procedure is to rely on previous performance.

The present-day forecaster actually usually employs a combination of both viewpoints. His primary tool is a chart or map showing the distribution of air pressure over his area of the earth. When based on many barometric readings, such a chart represents a real physical situation of the atmosphere. It gives vital information about the movement of air masses during the next few days, permitting winds and temperatures to be predicted with considerable accuracy if all disturbing influences are noted—the earth's out-of-kilter axis, its rotation which causes great curving air movements instead of direct flow, the earth's division into land and sea areas and the mountain ranges that divert the lower air layers. The chart is of little value in predicting whether or not rain or snow will fall tomorrow. Though it may suggest that thundercloud activity is likely in a general vicinity, the chart is of no value whatsoever in locating thundershowers, for these pop up as randomly as bubbles in a pot of boiling water. Weather prediction is still much an empirical and an intuitive process drawn from past experience.

Not surprisingly, the professional forecaster's batting average presently can be described as only fair. The United States Weather Bureau claims 85 per cent correctness, though a substantial part of the score is built up during periods of little change, thus easily predicted conditions. But there is every reason to expect great strides to be made in all meteorological endeavors in the not-too-distant future, for the science spurts forward in step with advances in apparently unrelated fields. The telegraph, it will be recalled, launched the science of meteorology. Much of our present knowledge of clouds, air masses, and storm development came from probing the air with airplanes, in the beginning an invention far removed from weather processes. Radar, with which the movement of storm and other clouds can be watched from quite some distance away, is currently the biggest boon that weathermen enjoy. The

Plate 1

The Earth As It Appears from a Rocket. One and one-quarter million square miles of the earth's area and its system of clouds are visible. From Omaha, Nebraska, on the horizon at the left to the lower Gulf of California on the right, the photograph covers parts of nine states and the whole of Texas. It is believed to contain the first photograph of a complete hurricane. In the upper left-hand portion of the picture the hurricane's giant swirl of clouds is evident. *Official U.S. Navy photograph.*

Satellite Television and the Weather. A view of the earth taken from a V-2 rocket at about sixty miles altitude. Through photographs such as this, the meteorologist will soon be able to get a global picture of the earth's clouds and weather each day.
Courtesy of Applied Physics Laboratory, The Johns Hopkins University.

Plate 2

Jet Stream Clouds. Racing along at better than 190 miles per hour, these jet stream clouds swept over Schenectady, New York, on March 2, 1953. *Courtesy Dr. Vincent J. Schaefer.*

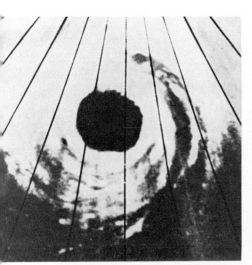

Left. *Radar Photograph of a Hurricane.* The thirty-five-mile wide, perfectly formed "eye" of typhoon Agnes which threatened to hit Okinawa in November 1952 is shown. By detecting the cloud structure, radar permitted this photograph to be made while the storm, with winds of more than 170 miles an hour, was approximately 120 miles from the island. *U.S. Air Force photograph.*

Right. *Inside a Hurricane's Eye.* This low-altitude view of a tropical storm cloud wall shows the ominous, churning black clouds. The center, or "eye," is to the right. *U.S. Air Force photograph.*

Plate 3

Several Waterspouts Observed Simultaneously. Photographed from a drilling platform some six miles south of Grand Isle, Louisiana, on May 19, 1948. *Courtesy of Humble Oil and Refining Company, Houston, Texas.*

Left. *Tornado.* This tornado cut a more or less continuous path nearly 400 feet in width and about sixteen miles long through the western parts of Dallas, Texas, on April 2, 1957. The incipient funnel at the right never reached the ground. About forty minutes elapsed after the primary funnel first touched the ground before it dissipated.
Courtesy of American Airlines, Dallas, Texas.

Right. *Lightning.* A July storm over the Rincon Mountains about twenty miles east of Tucson, Arizona.
Robert Riddell, FPG.

Plate 4

Upper left. *Unusual Cloud Formations.* These vortical formations were photographed over Marseilles, France; such clouds are often reported as flying saucers. *Wide World Photos.*

Upper right. *Halo Around the Sun.* Around either the sun or moon, this phenomenon presages rain or snow in a day or so. *Wide World Photos.*

Lower left. *Sun Pillar.* This apparition was seen from Yorkshire, England, near sunset. *Courtesy of C. A. Wood.*

Lower right. *Cloud Cap Atop Giant Column of Smoke.* The cloud was produced from moisture rising from a California brush and timber fire of September, 1956. *Wide World Photos.*

Plate 5

Left. *Low-Hanging Clouds.* From the sixty-ninth floor of the RCA Building, one can see above the heavy clouds that have descended on Manhattan. *Wide World Photos.*

Upper. *Mammato Cumulus Clouds.* Seldom seen and not completely understood. These appeared around 6:00 P.M. over Toulon, Illinois, on August 17, 1948.
Courtesy of Ernest Robson.

Roll Clouds. If adjacent layers of air move at different velocities as they did at Kew, England, on September 3, 1951, they tend to roll the clouds between them into rows.
Courtesy of Kenneth Woodley.

Wave-Cloud Formation. This unusual cloud structure occurred over Denver, Colorado, February 14, 1953.
Courtesy of Paul E. Branstine.

Hole in the Sky. A striking half-mile-wide opening in the clouds occurred over Knoxville, Tennessee, on February 23, 1957. It was produced when a higher mass of air dropped through a layer of clouds.
Wide World Photos.

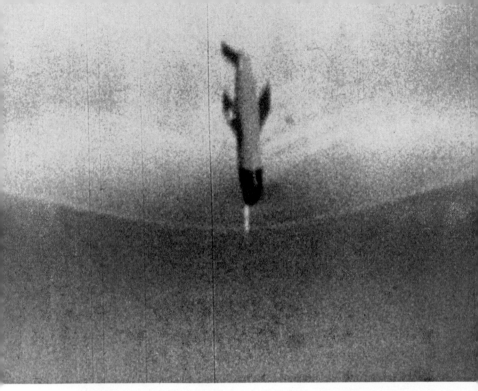

Plate 6

Top. *Shock Wave.* A Navy missile, Regulus I, is clearly preceded by a shock wave. This phenomenon, usually photographed only in wind tunnel tests, was recorded when the missile was plummeting earthward at a speed of approximately 800 miles per hour over California's Salton Sea.
Official U.S. Navy photograph.

Typical Cloud Formations. The fluffy white clouds at A are composed of water droplets; they might be altered by seeding. The thin wispy clouds at B are composed of ice crystals; seeding would have no effect on them.
Courtesy of the National Research Council, Canada.

Plate 7

Polluted Air over New York City. The accumulation of smoke and dirty air that hovers over most densely populated and industrialized areas is evident here.   *Courtesy of Interstate Sanitation Commission, Conn., N. J., N. Y.*

Smog in Donora. The photograph, taken on October 30, 1948, shows Donora, Pa., smothered in a stagnant mixture of smoke and gases. *Wide World Photos.*

Plate 8

Cloud Formation Following Thermonuclear Detonation. Photograph was taken fifty miles from detonation site. In twelve minutes the cloud stem pushed upward about twenty-five miles. The mushroom portion rose to ten miles and eventually spread for one hundred miles.
U.S. Air Force photograph.

Rocket Releasing Sodium into the Upper Atmosphere. Photographs were taken thirty seconds apart. The twisting and turning of the sodium trail was caused by varying wind velocities at different altitudes.
Courtesy of the Geophysics Research Directorate, Air Force Cambridge Research Center, Air Research and Development Command.

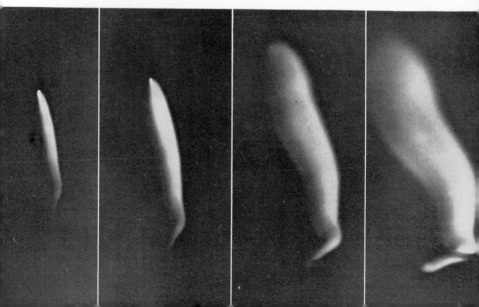

most useful, recent development here is a radar with a memory that greatly facilitates the charting of cloud development and front progression. At any time, the radarscope picture can be electronically recorded in a memory tube. Then ten to thirty minutes later the picture can be called back, superimposed on the clouds displayed at the moment. The remembered picture is presented in red while the current picture is green. Overlapping areas that indicate the change thus show in yellow due to the mixing of the primary colors.

Close behind and rapidly becoming of major importance are electronic machines that have stored within their memories just what events followed a particular weather situation some time previously. From them can be gotten in a matter of minutes a fair prediction of the weather likely to follow in the next few days. Also electronic computers that can make millions of computations involving complex relationships are being put into service. Into these are soon to be fed wind velocities, wind directions, and temperatures from a large number of observation stations scattered throughout the Northern Hemisphere. From the computers will come predicted winds and temperatures at specified times in the future. Already such predictions are being made from the reports of a limited number of stations, with results approximately as satisfactory as forecasts made by conventional methods. Future electronic calculations will remove many of the human factors from weather predicting. Into these machines in a few years will be fed air pressures, wind directions, precipitation zones, temperatures, air-mass boundaries, nuclei data, solar variations, and the particular weather characteristics of an area; and from them will come reasonably accurate predictions of the weather for coming days and months.

Perhaps an even greater future development involves earth satellites. From a vantage of two to three hundred miles and circling the earth each ninety minutes, these vehicles, using electronic eyes, can keep a close watch on the world's weather. They can spy on the birth of warm air masses by the cloud they spot, and they can report the first signs of warm air leaving its spawning area. They can give the location of weather fronts, where rain and snow are falling, where snow is receding, and where its coverage is expanding. In fact, they are potentially more valuable than would be a world-wide network of land and sea weather stations, long the dream of weathermen.

Future long-range weather forecasts will require careful attention to phenomena now only superficially observed. The gigantic storms that rage across the sun's surface are believed to have a pronounced effect on the world's weather, long cycles of sun storms undoubtedly influencing climatic changes on the earth and being partially responsible for its droughts and deluges. It may be that the paths of meteoric dust that the earth regularly traverses also influence precipitation.

When weather prophets of earlier times analyzed the behavior of spiders, leeches, ground hogs, tree frogs, plants, lunar phases, and the like, nothing could be relied upon, although occasionally someone would attain fleeting fame by happening to predict the coldest day of the year or a heavy flood. Even fifty years ago the weather forecasts of the meteorologists were largely a joke. Now businessmen, sportsmen, farmers, and ranchers rely on them as never before, and thousands of dollars may depend on advance weather information. A freshly poured concrete highway is damaged by rain, but hard to finish if the air is too dry; utility companies are caught short if an unforetold cold wave develops; seats are easy to obtain at the local baseball parks when rain is expected. Will the growing season be long or short, wet or dry? Will tomorrow be too windy for structural or roofing work? These are questions for which answers are ever needed. Truly reliable weather predictions, both long- and short-range, would be worth millions.

The weather is more than an economic matter, however. Like the fishes in the sea, we are susceptible to every change in our environment. Every fluctuation in the thermometer and barometer is followed by a shift in human and animal behavior. City police know they must expect an outbreak of illogical crimes with every heat wave, for people then are more quarrelsome, their nerves more frayed, their tempers more edgy. Suicides, altercations, and murders increase before storms and drop after them. Scholastic performance of students increases with the passage of fronts. When a cold front approaches our bodies adjust so as to insulate against the cooler condition. The liver releases sugar to give energy, blood pressure rises, muscle tone improves, and the metabolic rate increases. Deaths are more frequent in unsettled than in settled weather conditions because a diseased body may not be able to make or to tolerate rapid changes. All of us do less and poorer quality work some days than others; sometimes fatigue comes faster; sometimes we have more accidents. Humid days make us feel dull, the explanation being that then the tissues of our bodies take up water and swell somewhat like a wetted sponge, but brain tissue, being encased in a rigid bony cavity, cannot readily expand and contract. At the other extreme, bright sunny days improve our dispositions and even make our IQ's higher, especially just after a thunderstorm. We need to study the weather in order to understand ourselves.

11 weather according to plan

> *But methought it lessened my esteem
> of a king, that he should not be able
> to command the rain.*
>
> SAMUEL PEPYS

IF THERE is one power everyone has craved at some time, it is surely to control the weather. Recently it was said—somewhat facetiously to be sure—that it may be easier to control the weather than to predict it. While neither goal is likely ever to be achieved to our complete satisfaction, local weather modification has been attained and eventual control over some of the weather's particular manifestations is inevitable.

As far back as history records, man has exercised ingenuity to remake the weather to his liking. Believing the elements to reflect the vagaries and humors of their gods, primitive peoples solicited changes by incantations and sacrifices. Our American Indians smoked pipes and discharged arrows toward the clouds to start and stop rain. To cause the wind to blow, some tribes flapped their blankets; to halt a blizzard, another daubed a man with red paint who then, by rolling over and over in the snow, showed the suffering the blizzard was causing by the magnitude of the tinted space around him. Still another tribe had a company of men who ran to the top of a nearby hill with bows and arrows, magic drums, and other paraphernalia when a storm threatened. By their firing arrows, whooping, yelling, beating drums, and whistling, the rising cloud was supposed to be frightened down again. On at least one occasion witnessed by white men, a bright flash of lightning killed a member of the party during his act of shaking a spear at the cloud, thereby considerably lessening the ardor of others for the job.

Leaning more to religion, southern Russians at one time drenched their priest, hoping the message that rain was needed would be conveyed through him. The Armenians, possibly to avoid an encounter with a physically able priest, dunked the wives instead. A particularly vivid display and one the meaning of which could hardly be mistaken was provided by the Estonians, who believed the weather to be human in nature. Firebrands, a kettle, and pails of water were carried into a tree; then "lightning" was created in the form of the flaming brands, "thunder" by a tremendous bang on the kettle, and "rain" by emptying the pails. It is not recorded, however, that these endeavors were more successful than any of a vast number of others that might be listed.

Inevitably, as scientific knowledge developed, more direct schemes were concocted, but the early ones were hardly less fantastic than those based on superstition. To ameliorate winter cold, a line of stoves along our northern border from the Red River to the Continental Divide was seriously proposed at one time. In 1887 a United States patent was granted for an explosion system to destroy tornadoes. Probably suggested by the oft-told but unsubstantiated tale that a waterspout could be dissipated by cannon fire, the patent described a box filled with explosive to be erected on a pole a mile or so southwest of the town it was to protect. Through a suitable mechanism, a high wind such as that of a tornado was supposed to set off a powerful explosion and eliminate the tornado much like a rat throwing a trap. Before the turn of the present century, rain-making had been dignified by at least two United States patents, two congressional appropriations, two books, and a great many pamphlets. Though men at the time were still far from being able to exert any real control over the atmospheric machine, fumbling beginnings were being made. They were learning something of the forces at work in the weather.

Rain-making is really the granddaddy of all where weather control is concerned. It has attracted more attention, been subjected to more tests, and has a longer history than any other weather endeavor. A Pennsylvania meteorologist, James P. Espy, extolled great conflagrations as rain-producers in publications between 1838 and 1857. Being familiar with the fact that rains follow extensive forest fires, and perhaps having read an account published in 1784 by a Jesuit missionary to South America telling how Indians there produced rain by setting fire to the vegetation of the plains, Espy proposed that every seven days during the summer forest fires amounting to at least forty acres each twenty miles be kindled along a six- or seven-hundred-mile line in the west to start rain, which he felt certain would spread all the way to the Atlantic. The testimony on which Espy built his case is extremely interesting, even if his suggestion must be regarded as a little drastic and generally impractical.

His most enlightening account relates how surveyors working the east coast of Florida found that respite from the oppressive heat of early summer in the year 1845 could be relieved by setting fire to densely matted, highly inflammable saw grass. The initial discovery came quite by chance. To avoid cutting through a five-hundred-acre tract one day in April, the surveyors set the covering grass afire. Neither an aspen leaf stirred nor was there a cloud in the sky when the fire started. Soon a fierce blaze with flames soaring above the tallest trees spread across the area. Shortly thereafter a delightful breeze sprang up, and presently a cooling shower fell. Burning the grass then became standard operating procedure for the surveyors. Sometimes the rain fell in torrents; sometimes it fell when clear sky could be seen all around except above the smoke and clouds immediately overhead; and at other times, when a breeze was blowing, rain could be seen falling on the horizon toward which the smoke drifted. The surveyors further reported that at no times during April or May other than after one of their fires did rain fall.

In Europe particularly it became popular to associate rain after battles with the concussions of heavy cannonading. Accordingly, fifty to seventy-five years ago many attempts were made to cause rain with explosives. Explosions on the ground and in the air, great single explosions, volleys of explosions, and even explosions of gas-filled balloons were tried. None were successful, but they led to other endeavors.

Though it involved an explosion and was not conceived as such, an approach that was something more than a frontal assault on nature was carried out by Louis Gathmann of Chicago in 1890. Having worked on the problem of cooling large artillery pieces and being interested in explosions as a means of jarring rain from the clouds, Gathmann combined his ideas and filled a shell with carbon dioxide under pressure, which would become very cold dry ice upon release. When the shell burst in the clear sky, the observers were elated to see a cloud form, which, drifting in the air, remained visible for miles. This result, though failing to produce downpours as hoped, was taken as proof of the concussion approach. As we shall see later, the true cause was something else again. Nevertheless a hint had been obtained that would eventually bear fruit.

In 1923 the world's imagination was aroused by a series of scientific experiments as it had been at no time previously. L. Francis Warren announced that he and associates had invented a scheme for dispersing fogs and clouds. Conceiving clouds to be composed of electrified particles (see Chapter 6) which needed only to be brought together into larger drops, these gentlemen doctored clouds with electrified sand discharged from an airplane. For a year and a half they experimented at McCook Field near Dayton, Ohio, and indeed succeeded in dispersing some fogs. From the practical standpoint their efforts proved to be relatively unimportant, however. Large quantities of sand were required to produce rather meager results.

Again in 1930 considerable attention was attracted by rain-making efforts in Holland. Using a technique probably influenced by the earlier experiments of Gathmann but still holding to the electrified-sand idea that changes were predominant in congealing the clouds into rain, August W. Veraart dropped huge quantities of dry ice, solid carbon dioxide, from an airplane into clouds and into the open atmosphere. Because key points of cloud phenomena were misunderstood at the time, his dry ice was used ineffectively and the results were inconsistent. Weather modification lapsed once more into the background. Observation continued and forecasting was improved, but ever doing anything about the weather became a rather heretical idea.

The more or less passive science into which meteorology then developed was shattered finally in the mid-1940's by experiments started in the General Electric Company's Schenectady laboratories. While working on the problem of deadly ice formation on airplane wings during World War II, Nobel Prize winner Irving Langmuir and his colleague Vincent Schaefer studied the water droplets in high, cold clouds which caused the icing trouble. They came to suspect that these unfrozen cloud droplets held answers to important meteorological questions, among them: Why does it rain? As soon as the war with its urgent military problems ended, work on rain clouds was begun in earnest.

A most intriguing property of clouds is that they sometimes exist in what is known as a supercooled state—that is, with their droplets unfrozen even though their temperature is far below the normal freezing point for water of 32 degrees Fahrenheit. Although the supercooled state can be produced in the laboratory, such unresponsive behavior for chilled water is foreign to our experience, because we always have it in contact with a slightly impure container whose walls furnish sites where freezing may start. In the open atmosphere water droplets, lacking such nucleating centers, do not freeze without considerable prodding. Once ice formation begins, however, it causes rapid changes in clouds, for supercooled droplets are as vulnerable to ice crystals as sheep to marauding wolves. The crystals steal water vapor from the droplets, thereby growing large and heavy. As others had before him, Langmuir reasoned that, if a relatively few ice crystals could be induced to form in supercooled clouds, they should grow large at the expense of the droplets, and eventually fall as snow or, melting on the way down, as rain. The magic ice-forming motes were thus sought as a key to the rain process.

In an ordinary home freezer illuminated with a bright light and lined with black velvet for better visibility, Schaefer experimented with miniature clouds, which were easily formed by blowing his breath into the freezer. All kinds of chemicals were tried with little success, until one day in July, 1946, to cool the chamber more rapidly, Schaefer put in a chunk of dry ice, its temperature being minus 110 degrees Fahrenheit. Immediately a myriad of glistening crystals swirled in the light beam, and, as he watched, they grew into snowflakes and dropped to the bottom. A way of playing midwife to pregnant clouds had been revealed!

On November 13, 1946, Schaefer and a pilot went hunting for real supercooled clouds in a small plane. Over Massachusetts they sighted a fleecy one, four miles across and aimlessly drifting along. Into it Schaefer scattered six pounds of dry ice. Almost at once the cloud began to writhe and to swell with blisterlike white protrusions suggestive of thunderheads. Within five minutes only a thin wreath of snow showed where the cloud had been. Drifting eastward, the snow soon disappeared, leaving no visible remains of the cloud whatsoever.

Throughout the following winter, spreading dry ice from airplanes produced snow flurries and cut great grooves and holes in solid decks of stratified clouds. The feats were dramatic and rewarding, but they were not all Langmuir and Schaefer sought. In addition to requiring an airplane, the dry ice was effective only while falling through the clouds; and even then, if the ice particles did not take effect immediately, they evaporated and were lost.

But all the while another colleague, Bernard Vonnegut, was seeking a permanent nonvolatile particle to replace dry ice. On the hypothesis that the most likely crystal would be one having structural dimensions like ice, silver iodide, the closest of those readily available, was tested. Sure enough, a few specks evaporated off an electrically heated wire converted a cloud in a freezer chamber into snow. The merest trace of the iodide seemed to work miracles. The problem then became one of designing a generator capable of producing billions of tiny silver iodide particles per second. This was soon accomplished, and airplane flights from which silver iodide was released produced an effect on supercooled clouds just as dry ice had done. Indications were obtained, moreover, that silver iodide nuclei released from the ground modified certain clouds when the nuclei drifted into them. The team of Langmuir, Schaefer, and Vonnegut now sought to demonstrate to the world the potential benefits of its discoveries. Though it has now been shown beyond all doubt that some clouds can be made to precipitate by "seeding" them with silver iodide particles, widespread rain-making is yet to be established.

Among a great many tests, only two are required to indicate the type and nature of seeding results. Choosing the Southwest because all the rain formed there would be appreciated, because frontal storms do not as often spread across that area as across many others, and because prevailing winds would carry any effect eastward across much of the nation, Langmuir and company started a silver iodide generator located on the ground near Albuquerque, New Mexico, early one morning in July, 1949. Developments were followed by weather-observing radar. By 8:30 A.M. a cloud in an otherwise cloudless sky appeared about twenty-five miles away downwind. Upon reaching an altitude of 26,000 feet, the cloud spurted upward at fifteen miles per hour. Soon thereafter the radar echo showed the cloud to be full of rain or snow, and some time later heavy rains fell near the Manzano Mountains, some distance farther away. Calculating that the wind velocity was about right to carry his silver iodide particles into the cloud just at the time it developed, Langmuir took credit for the rain. There are reasons to be skeptical, however. No one can be certain that the rain would not have come anyway. Among other reasons for skepticism is the fact, not at first recognized, that strong sunlight works a partial deactivating spell on the silver iodide. In this case the particles were exposed, though the early morning light would not have been intense.

The most ambitious experiment, and one still heatedly debated, was carried out by the same investigators over eighty-two weeks between December, 1949, and July, 1951. From a ground-based generator at Socorro, New Mexico, about one-half pound of silver iodide was released into the air during eight hours of operation each Tuesday, Wednesday, and Thursday. This prearranged schedule was designed so that, if successful, a seven-day periodicity would be introduced into weather cycles and objections about specific clouds would be nullified.

Within two weeks after the start of this experiment, statisticians began to detect weekly changes in rainfall, cloudiness, temperatures, and pressures in the Mississippi Valley. By the spring of 1950, with the advent of heavy rains, some of which seemed to follow a seven-day cycle, and floods in the Midwest, the experimenters, fearful that they were partially responsible, reduced their seeding rate and asked a committe of meteorologists to examine the data then available. After examination, the committee declared the correlation accidental, and full-scale silver iodide generation was resumed.

Final Weather Bureau records for the period show that an unmistakable seven-day cycle tendency did prevail in almost every state of the Union at least part of the period, and that the effect was most pronounced in states along the Mississippi and Ohio rivers, the area over which the prevailing winds would have carried much of the silver iodide and mixed it with moisture-laden clouds moving north from the Gulf of Mexico. This evidence suggests that the weather indeed was made to dance to the rhythm of the seeding, to a tune for which the piper's pay was a paltry daily handful of silver iodide. Few experiments in modern times have seemed to prove so much, yet again the results can be accepted at face value by scientists only with reluctance. There are indeed difficulties to be examined. Unfortunately, to resolve the difficulties now will require years of weather observation.

In October, 1950, the schedule of silver iodide generation was shifted, yet the weather did not respond as earlier indications suggested it should have. According to Langmuir, this obscuring of results was due to the fact that by now other "rain-makers" were operating silver iodide generators around the country. Though this may have been the cause, it is not an established fact. Also periodicity is not unknown in the weather's behavior, and there is reason to doubt that silver iodide retains its effectiveness long enough to find its way across half the continent. It can only be lamented that commercial cloud-seeders came into being before the technique was established or disproved.

Now, years later, and despite elaborate claims of professional rain-makers whose paying customers represent timberland owners, power companies, and farmer combines covering large segments of the West, Midwest, and South, the evidence for widespread rain production is still unsettled. Over flat, normally dry country particularly, results generally have not been spectacular. It is in cold weather and over mountain ranges, which force the air to rise, that cloud-seeding seems to be most effective. Obviously, before rain or snow can be produced anywhere the atmosphere must contain a lot of moisture. When one removes from contention those clouds that are precipitating, those that are not at the proper temperature, and those that are at nucleating temperatures but in layers so thin that the resulting raindrops are small and will evaporate before reaching the ground, it is doubtful if seeding can be expected to produce more than a 15 per cent increase in rainfall [Plate 6]. This being the case, it will be years before weather data reveal if the over-all pattern of rain has actually been increased and if the cause is due to the rain-makers' efforts or simply to a wetter weather cycle, of which there have been many in the past.

Whether or not cloud-seeding proves to be economically feasible, it has established that doing something about the weather is possible and opened weather science to tremendous research efforts, which already are paying dividends. We now know much of the life history of a raindrop. Before a cloud forms there must be an upsurge of millions of tons of air. As the mass cools by expansions, it causes condensation of water vapor to occur on some of the wide variety of solid particles, which are present everywhere throughout the lower atmosphere in amounts of a thousand or so per thimbleful of air. These particles share the available water vapor about equally, so the resulting cloud is composed of droplets averaging at most a few ten-thousandths of an inch across. Since a normal raindrop is equivalent to something like a million of these cloud droplets, dramatic transformation is required to convert the multitude of droplets into drops.

In tropical and subtropical zones relatively large drops come into being by coalescence of much smaller ones. A droplet that is larger than the average begins to fall. In so doing it collides and coalesces with some of those lying in its path, becoming larger. Its fall continues at an ever increasing rate. When the small-droplet population is sufficiently great and the larger droplet's journey in the cloud is sufficiently long, the drop eventually grows great enough to fall as rain. Even in temperate zones during warm weather some rain starts in this fashion; most, however, passes through an ice-crystal process.

Particles on which water vapor readily condenses are not necessarily good promoters of freezing. Prominent varieties, sea-salt crystals particularly, dissolve and may actually hinder freezing for the same reason that antifreeze in an automobile radiator affords cold-weather protection. As described previously, a fundamental feature of natural water clouds in cooler climates is their frequent occurrence with their droplets still liquid but their temperature well below freezing. At just below the freezing point, the probability of a droplet happening upon a solid nucleus that will promote freezing is negligibly small, but at lower temperatures the

probability increases until at a minus 40 degrees Fahrenheit droplets will freeze spontaneously; hence, dry ice's point of value is its
low temperature.

A variety of dust particles, however, become capable of initiat-
ing crystallization of supercooled water droplets above this spon-
taneous-freezing temperature. To name a few examples, Nevada soil
particles become active ice-nucleating agents at about minus 20
degrees, Georgia clay at minus 16 degrees, Mexican volcanic ash at
minus 15 degrees, Colorado sand at minus 4 degrees, North Dakota
loam at plus 3 degrees. Silver iodide becomes active at plus 23
degrees Fahrenheit, but its effective temperature is reduced considerably by strong sunlight. Its cousin, lead iodide, promotes
freezing at only a couple of degrees lower and it is unaffected by
sunlight. In general, then, ice crystals form in supercooled clouds
at temperatures set by the character of the prevalent nuclei.

Clearly there is reason to expect many natural clouds to succumb to silver iodide, or better still, lead iodide seeding. Just as
clearly, there is reason to believe that a little more cooling would
produce rain via the natural nuclei. Herein lies the crux of the
arguments over cloud-seeding techniques. It is not denied that adding nuclei will produce rain in some cases; it is a question of the
degree to which rain would have come naturally without man's
interference.

As knowledge of the coalescence process in warm tropical clouds
has developed, other seeding ideas have been tried. In this case the
need is not for nuclei to promote freezing but for relatively large
drops or particles on which raindrops can develop. One obvious
solution is simply to spray water into a cloud from a tank carried
by an airplane. Recent Australian experiments of this very type
have been encouraging; ten out of eleven trials in which a few
hundred gallons of water were sprayed into susceptible-appearing
clouds produced rain, and in four cases the precipitation could be
classed as heavy. Similar tests in the Caribbean have also met with
some success. Like earlier dry-ice seeding, the economics of this
method requiring an airplane may seriously limit its acceptance.

Nevertheless, another type of cloud-coaxing is being tried in drought-stricken western Australia. A plane trailing two three-hundred-foot cables on which is impressed a fifty-thousand-volt electric charge is to be drawn through clouds in an attempt to charge the droplets and make them coalesce.

Other techniques are being devised to operate from ground level. In East Africa balloon-borne bombs containing a mixture of gun-powder and finely ground salt have been released to drift into the clouds, there to burst and scatter salt crystals about. In Pakistan, where the climate is extremely dry, salt dust has been blown into the air or simply spread along the roads to be kicked up by passing traffic. Though the results are far from conclusive, both methods seem to justify further exploration.

There is also a possibility that clouds can be overseeded to pro-duce such desirable results as mitigation of hail and lightning, per-haps someday floods. Every year hail ruins millions of dollars' worth of crops. In this country alone, lightning destroys an average of sixteen million acres of timber, and floods cause $275,000,000 worth of property damage. Like poisons, which in small doses are fatal yet in larger doses result in vomiting and expulsion of the poison, too many nuclei may check the more violent weather effects. If a great number of nuclei are competing for the available water vapor of a cloud, none may be able to grow to raindrop size.

At Longkloof, on the eastern cape of South Africa, farmers have for several years regularly been firing French-made rockets loaded with silver iodide into thunderclouds. So far they have had only harmless rain fall from menacing hail clouds that in past years laid waste the important apple crop. The theory of the operation—at the present it must be called a theory—is that the silver iodide accelerates the precipitation process so that large hailstones have no chance to develop. Controlled silver iodide seeding seems also to have reduced hail in what were formerly hailstorm centers of the Midwest.

Overseeding also holds promise of producing rain under par-ticular circumstances. In Arizona during the summer, rains seldom fall in any amount unless the atmosphere contains enough moisture to produce more than one inch of rain; clouds with lesser amounts usually drift away without precipitating. During the summer of 1957 heavy seeding with silver iodide was tested on the hypothesis that some of the clouds might be induced to remain and continue growing, thus producing more rain when finally rain did fall. Results seem to confirm the expectations. On seeded days rainfall surpassed that of unseeded ones by about 15 per cent, and, significantly, eight of the nine days during the test showing maximum rains of one inch or more were those on which seeding was employed.

Lightning modification is currently being studied in the Coconino National Forest, a relatively isolated section of Arizona, where lightning starts hundreds of fires annually. Mobile radar is used to detect and analyze the storms, and ground-level iodide generators, as well as small aircraft equipped with high-output generators, throw the particles into likely storm clouds. No results are in from this work, but earlier experiments in which minute traces of ammonia and ammonium compounds were introduced into clouds along with silver iodide gave evidence of a diminution of electric effects. There is thus hope for lightning's control and also a suggestion that atmospheric contaminants may play a significant role in lightning. In a decade we may see a situation in which an incipient storm is detected in a particular area and then rendered harmless by suitable measures.

Seeding efforts, for all their versatility, are aimed at only one point of the meteorological cycle; intervening at other points where nature is vulnerable may be even more advantageous in the long run. It will be recalled that the atmosphere is a kind of gigantic engine that distributes to polar regions some of the excess heat from the sun falling on equatorial parts of the earth. It does so by the air's circulation and by the thermodynamic process of evaporating and condensing water. In principle at least, the weather can be altered by interfering either with the balance between heat received and heat lost to space by radiation, or with the evaporation-condensation cycle.

The obvious way of interfering with incoming radiation would be to reflect a part of it away. There can be little doubt that a stratospheric blanket of dust or smoke would have to be only moderately dense to cut off an appreciable fraction of solar radiation. It will be remembered (Chapter 7) that a pall of smoke from a Canadian forest fire passed over Europe in September, 1950. In its path, maximum daily temperatures were reduced as much as 10 degrees. If a uniform cloud were produced (about a million tons of material would be required according to one calculation) at stratospheric levels, it would persist for quite some time and surface temperatures would certainly be lowered. Attendant changes would occur also in atmospheric circulation, storminess, and rainfall.

If more instead of less heat were desired, this too might be achieved. Of course we cannot increase the sun's output, but we can arrange for less of it to be radiated away from the earth. Polar ice and snow are relatively good reflectors of sunlight energy, as well as radiators of the earth's internal heat. But if these areas were covered with a microscopically thin layer of colored matter, perhaps black soot, the reflection-radiation process would be upset. More of the ice would melt, altering local weather conditions certainly, and world-wide conditions very probably.

It has been reported that Russia has increased her usable agricultural area by aerial springtime dusting of snow-covered lands with powdered coal. Another test of this type is being readied. A French meteorologist plans to clear a section in the center of a Congo coconut palm plantation and cover it with charcoal. Heat absorbed from the sun is then expected to make the area very hot in comparison to the surrounding forest. Rising currents of heated air should thus start upward and, it is hoped, pull along sufficient outlying air to form clouds when cooler levels of the atmosphere are reached. If clouds but no rain are produced, seeding will be added to coax rainfall. Recalling the century-old reports of the Florida surveyors, the plan cannot be called ill-conceived. Also experiences of World War II pilots in the Pacific lend credence to it. From early morning until late in the afternoon, tiny islands and atolls could be located long before the land appeared by the clouds that hung in patches over them. The cause of such clouds was precisely the same as hoped for in Africa—areas of heated land in the midst of surrounding cooler ocean.

Still another method of using heat absorption to remake the weather more to our liking has been demonstrated by Navy scientists, this time using very fine particles of carbon discharged into the atmosphere from an airplane. In tests conducted along the Georgia coast, clouds were both dispelled and formed. When a pound and a half of finely-divided carbon was sprinkled on top of a large cloud, one extending from 5000 to an elevation of 11,000 feet and rising, it disappeared in twenty minutes. But when carbon was spread throughout a moist layer of air at about 4000 feet clouds appeared where none had been before. Apparently in the first instance the carbon acquired enough of the sun's heat to overcome the cooling occasioned by the cloud's rising to higher altitudes, while in the second the absorption of heat introduced a thermal instability that resulted in a rising column of air. Clouds subsequently developed when the air attained higher and cooler altitudes. Whether effects might be produced with powdered carbon under other conditions remains to be seen, but dispelling fog and breaking up thunderstorms and hurricanes are possibilities.

Alteration of the hydrological cycle, the evaporation-condensation tempo, is also a distinct possibility. As in previous cases, we may be able either to "pull or push." Large-scale irrigation projects, by impounding vast acres of water in reservoirs, would create new water surfaces from which vapor could escape. It follows directly that the more water vapor is created, the more rain must fall somewhere. Conversely, impeding the loss of water from existing lakes and seas must inevitably decrease precipitation. Here, thin films of chemicals are required. In quiet pools, almost infinitesimal quantities of certain alcohols spread in films over the water only a few molecules thick have been found to reduce evaporation by some 40 per cent. Large-scale trials to impede evaporation from wind-disturbed lakes are in progress in Australia and in this country at

Rattlesnake Reservoir in Colorado. They are certainly worth following with interest.

The tremendous energies that are now potentially available in the hydrogen bomb are a factor to be considered, though behind-the-scenes schemes such as those already mentioned are much more likely to be feasible in the foreseeable future than any direct pitting of force against force. It is true, however, that the underwater explosion at Bikini in July, 1946, ejected large quantities of water and steam and caused sufficient lifting of local tropical air to produce rain that lasted for nearly thirty minutes. Following the explosion at Hiroshima and the fires that broke out everywhere, a severe storm developed. Even "fire storms" followed World War II incendiary-bomb raids on Hamburg, Kassel, Darmstadt, and Dresden. Over Hamburg a column of heated air one and one-half miles in diameter rose two and one-half miles high. As it did so, air from surrounding areas was pulled in with such force that trees three feet in diameter were uprooted. Significant as these events were, they were transient and localized. With bombs of the present magnitude, the feasibility of altering large areas of the atmosphere by brute force almost vanishes, for it will be recalled that the earth receives energy from the sun equivalent to one hydrogen bomb each second. A hurricane is equivalent to several hundred hydrogen bombs, and even a modest thunderstorm involves as much energy as several atom bombs.

The energy that clouds involve can perhaps be brought even better into proper perspective if it is pointed out that an inch of rain on a garden fifty feet wide and one hundred feet in length means 25,000 pounds of water. A yearly rainfall of forty-five inches is not unusually large; yet, if spread uniformly throughout the year, the daily mass of water falling on a square mile would be nearly nine thousand tons. In a year Manhattan Island receives over seventy million tons of water. It goes without saying that a pump that will lift such quantities thousands of feet must be powerful indeed.

There are other factors with colossal bombs, however, that must at present be classed as unknown. Bomb explosions do produce great quantities of nuclei, and slightly radioactive rain has fallen as much as half a world away. Most likely the bomb's debris was largely washed from the air and had little or no part in the rain's production; in fact, a surplus of nuclei may have impeded rainfall, as suggested previously. Still, until the behavior of all types of nuclei are catalogued, the possibility of a slight effect cannot be ruled out arbitrarily. Since a ground-level hydrogen bomb explosion sends rather large quantities of dust into the stratosphere, such an explosion probably has a very slight effect on the weather because the dust reflects away a fraction of the sun's energy. Our March, 1954, explosion of a large bomb affords an example. Like the unusually cool period, brilliant red sunsets, and Bishop's rings (see Chapter 8) caused by the famous eruption of Krakatoa in 1883, the summer of 1954 seems to have come late to Japan and Bishop's rings were again noted there.

Possibly the most significant effect of nuclear-bomb tests on the weather is exerted in the least-apparent manner—through a change in the air's electric conductivity (see Chapter 6). Since 1954, there have occurred periods lasting several days when the air's ability to conduct electricity was decidedly increased. Since they coincided with bomb tests, the cause is thought to be the abnormal number of ions produced in nuclear explosions. Whether greater conductivity will mean fewer thunderstorms or greater numbers of them to compensate for the increased leakage of electricity, meteorologists can now only guess. They lean, however, toward the idea that the greater "leakiness" of the air may discourage thunderstorm development and thereby decrease global rainfall and cause a decline in lightning-produced nitrogen fertilizers—both serious effects, if true.

Hurricane experts are virtually certain that a hydrogen bomb, though often suggested, is no practical answer to a well-developed hurricane. In the first place, radioactivity would be added to the storm's other hazards; and in the second, instead of the one eliminating the other, their energies might combine into even greater destruction. But a young hurricane may have an Achilles' heel, and considerable effort and money is being expended to discover it. The few hurricanes that are spawned each year seem to have great difficulty getting started. Meteorologists are fairly certain that from every hundred or so weather situations favoring hurricane formation, only about one actually develops. It seems likely from this that certain very special conditions are required, and that there is hope of breaking up hurricanes before they start.

Seeding with dry ice, silver iodide, or salt is the method most discussed for destroying hurricanes in their lair, but because of an extremely unhappy experience that occurred on October 13, 1947, caution is the order. On that date 180 pounds of dry ice, costing $7.20, were dropped into a large hurricane then slowly moving northward about four hundred miles off the Georgia coast. Almost immediately the dry ice seemed to produce more rain, and soon some three hundred square miles of the hurricane's cloud deck was converted into ice crystals. Subsequently the hurricane turned sharply, sweeping inland over Savannah and wreaking damage of five million dollars. Whether the seeding actually caused the storm to veer is a moot question. Nevertheless, no one wished to take credit for its change of course, and evidence that a similar path was followed by a 1906 hurricane was hurriedly produced. Some scientists, notably Dr. Langmuir, were certain that the change was man-made. Some also see in the result the possibility that future hurricanes can be seeded lightly and steered out over northern seas, there ultimately to die of moisture starvation. Plans to such an end are being readied. This time, however, the doses will be cautiously administered and the effects watched as closely as a medical researcher watches his experiments with a new and dangerous drug.

It is really too soon to evaluate the significance of weather modification thus far, but all the evidence indicates the general aim to be an attainable one. The probability is strong that weather intervention will develop in a few decades and that its extent will be on a scale difficult to imagine at present. Weather control will raise great political problems, for the circulation of the world's atmosphere is such that any large-scale change, though desirable for one part of the world, might be detrimental to another. It is even conceivable that weather may be used as a weapon of war. By creating storms or dissipating them as required by a tactical situation, a deluge might be brought or needed rain withheld to destroy crops. Statements to the effect that a nation will soon dominate the globe by learning to control the weather nevertheless are quite premature.

At the thought of a future with the elements under control, some will cry, "Hold"! "Enough"! Many will voice the common fear of a dreadful fate awaiting anyone so rash as to tamper with the larger, more potent forces of nature. It has ever been so; primitive peoples' taboos and the mythology of antiquity bear abundant witness to it. Icarus, with wings of wax and feathers, flew too close to the sun and was destroyed. Prometheus was sentenced to everlasting torture for his act of stealing fire and bestowing its use upon mankind. In this twentieth century vaccines have been damned by some. Insecticides have been called by some merely devices for hastening a breed of superinsects over which we will have no control. Surely tampering with the weather can only end with the world's being a quasi-permanent desert, they will say!

Quite to the contrary, weather control, wisely used, could provide ample rain for all nations. It could remake arid areas into fertile plains. The uncertainty of farming could be largely removed. Just enough crops of the proper kind could be planted if the harvest were assured beforehand. The ravages of floods and droughts could be prevented. Northern winter resorts could be able to have snow from September to March, while southern ones could guarantee sunshine. Sooner than we expect, Mark Twain's remark that everybody talks about the weather but nobody does anything about it may have to be accompanied by a bit of explanation.

12 climate

Hot, cold, moist, and dry,
four champions fierce,
Strive here for mast'ry . . .
JOHN MILTON

CLIMATE IS the sum total of all the weather that occurs at any place. Like the weather, climates are directed by the sun and are influenced by all the physical conditions of the earth—the nearness of an ocean, the presence or absence of mountains, prevailing winds, and the like. Being composite quantities, the climates of particular localities are comparatively constant, for the atmosphere, despite pronounced and rapid changes, has an inherent character that causes the weather pattern to repeat itself time and again. Cold days occasionally occur in hot climates, and hot days are not unknown in cold climates; dry climates often have rainy periods, and wet ones long periods of drought. Even so, every place on the face of the earth exhibits its peculiar combination of heat and cold, rain and sunshine. Obviously it would be impossible to consider each locality in detail; but, within limits, we may examine the general types of climate that prevail about the earth, we may consider the effects of climates, and we may note past and future consequences of long-range climatic shifts.

Latitude is the most evident of all the factors establishing climatic conditions. Without exception the air is cold above the earth's poles. Only near the summits of a few high mountains are equatorial lands anything but hot. Poleward from the equator, climates as a rule pass successively from wet heat through dry heat to wet cold and, finally, dry cold. These are the four primary climates, but among them hybrids, variations, modifications, and peculiarities abound.

Much of the world's population lives in so-called temperate climates, two climatic belts encircling the earth between roughly 30 and 50 degrees latitude north and south. Of all climates these are the most changeable. In summer the temperate zones are either dry and hot or wet and hot. Thunderstorms dominate the sky and bring such irrigating rain as falls. Occasionally even during summer, a polar mass of air intrudes upon the area. As autumn approaches, polar air becomes more restless. At first mildly, but then with increasing authority, it exerts its influence. One day the weather is fair, maybe mild, while on the next ice or snow blankets the land. By winter the polar air is in nearly complete control.

Temperature changes from day to night and from winter to summer are both significant in the temperate zones. Both may vary widely from the long-term average. One winter may be as much as 8 to 10 degrees warmer or colder than the preceding one; summer heat may differ similarly. In addition to great variations of temperature, every conceivable hazard—hot and cold fronts, tornadoes, thunderstorms, hurricanes, sandstorms, dust storms, and snowstorms—are common in these zones. The real meaning, then, of the term temperate zone is "middle latitude," and its outstanding atmospheric feature is changefulness. In other words, the temperate zones are the seasonal belts of the world.

Poleward from the temperate zones are the polar regions, encompassing Siberia, northern Canada, Greenland, and Antarctica.

There are largely undeveloped areas waiting human exploitation, for they are neither uninhabitated nor uninhabitable. The Arctic, in particular, is an unbelievably fertile region in places. Plants grow with amazing rapidity in its twenty-four-hour summer sunlight. Vegetation appears in infinite variety, and mosquitoes abound as nowhere else on earth. But the area's weather can be as vicious as its mosquitoes. An occasional thunderstorm forms over even the northernmost lands in summer. Wintertime gales and blizzards can turn the region into a wilderness of ice and snow, while temperatures drop to between 70 and 90 degrees below zero Fahrenheit. Oddly, strong winds are infrequent, and the air is extremely stable for flying because surface cooling makes the air heavy at the bottom.

The sun's remaining above the horizon in summer, then hiding below it in winter, is as important a feature of the arctic scene as is the all-pervading wintertime cold. Though low in the sky even in midsummer, the sun sends down a great quantity of energy by working around the clock. On flat snow-covered ground much of this heat is reflected away, but southerly slopes warm up quickly in spring and the snow melts rapidly. These sites have a favorable local climate. The summers in continental arctic regions are short, cool, and generally dull. The average July temperature is about 40 degrees, but days in which the thermometer climbs to 70 degrees are not uncommon; frequent but not heavy showers of rain or snow occur. The average February temperature is about minus 25 degrees, but extremes go very much lower. Generally, wintertime weather is clear and there is not much snow because the air, being so cold, can contain relatively little moisture. In fact, the annual precipitation in the Arctic is less than in some desert areas. The Arctic gives the appearance of being a wasteland of lakes, bogs, and marshes only because the ground, permanently frozen a few feet down, impedes drainage.

Along the ice-bound arctic shores the climate is much more severe than in the interior though not as cold. The long winters are dreary, while the short summers are foggy and rainy. Where rivers flow into the Arctic Ocean, spring rains and melting snow result in ice jams and floods that make the country impassable. Where warm ocean currents wash the shores, as in southern Iceland and southwestern Spitsbergen, the climate is much more favorable. The coasts of Greenland are not especially cold in winter, and temperatures exceeding 70 degrees have been recorded there in summer. Antarctica, being an elevated land mass, is much colder and far stormier than the Arctic. Summer temperatures of zero are the order, and winter temperatures drop below minus 100 degrees Fahrenheit, the record low as reported by a team of Russian explorers being minus 114 degrees. Blizzards develop with surprising suddenness even in midsummer.

In direct contrast to the dry cold of polar regions is the wet heat of the equatorial belt that includes Central America, Brazil, the Congo, and the East Indies. Here the climate is perpetually hot, humid, and rainy, with but little difference between the hottest and coolest months and between night and day. Temperatures seldom rise above 100 and seldom drop below 60 degrees at moderate altitudes, but the high humidity makes the region something like a Turkish bath. Vegetation grows in chaotic profusion, and parasitic plant types abound in lush, crowded conditions. Metals corrode, and leather, paper, and cloth rapidly mold. The water-saturated air rises in steamy torrents, and thunderstorms dump floods of rain almost daily. Though thunderstorms are frequent and sometimes severe, other climatic catastrophes such as hurricanes and tornadoes are almost unknown.

Between the equatorial belt and the temperate zones, around 25 degrees of latitude, lie the hot but dry tropical regions. Upon these the air that rose in the equatorial belt descends after having been relieved of most of its moisture burden. The air is hot initially, and the descent serves further to heat it dynamically so that it figuratively sears the prostrate earth. The result is a string of deserts around the world—the Sahara, the Libyan, the Arabian, and the Great Australian—in which are found the highest temperatures and some of the driest conditions on the face of the globe. In the shade the air reaches 130 degrees, while the ground, soaking up the direct rays of the sun, is baked to as much as 170 degrees. Desert nights are cool. Differences of 60 degrees between day and night are not unusual, and because of the low humidity of the air the variation feels greater still. Rainfall is slight or even nonexistent; in the deserts of Peru there are places where rain has not been known to fall for centuries.

Sandstorms and dust storms are frequent in the larger deserts, notably the Sahara. Except after a rare rainstorm, low-level desert air seems to be filled perpetually with a fine haze of dust particles. On hot afternoons rising thermal currents of air create whirling pillars of sand, and when the wind is strong the ground itself seems to be in motion; walking is difficult at such times. Flying at low levels is often rough because the intense heating near the ground makes the air top-heavy, unstable, and bumpy. At high levels flying conditions are generally good across dry tropical climates because of excellent visibility in the cloudless skies.

The desert is not just a waste area of heat, sand, and wind. A rain causes plant life to spring up, grow to maturity, produce seed in the space of a very few days, and thus be ready to lie dormant again for years if necessary. Around wells and where irrigation brings water, the desert becomes a veritable garden. In parts of Egypt, Iraq, and our western United States, irrigation and abundant sunshine combine to produce crops throughout the year. Where water is available, as in Egypt and in our western irrigated lands, winter is a pleasant season.

Though the subject of climates has been introduced in terms of four distinct types, pure climates about the earth are nearly as rare as pure minerals within the earth's crust. A major cause of climate mongrelization is the annual pacing back and forth of the sun across the noonday sky. Hanging above the Tropic of Cancer in June, the sun's position shifts to look directly down upon the Tropic of Capricorn in December. With this shifting of solar-heat influx, climates too sway back and forth. One interesting feature of the change is that maximum temperatures lag a month or so behind the sun's position; that is, maximum average temperatures in the Northern Hemisphere occur in mid-July instead of mid-June. The causes of this behavior are complex, but they involve time for the earth's surface to warm and for the air itself to adjust its flow pattern about the globe.

Obviously, those areas caught between two climatic zones will receive a dose of both as the sun advances and retreats. Regions situated between wet and dry tropical climates come to have a half-and-half climate, called tropical monsoon. Typical monsoon areas include Burma and India, the African Sudan, and Northern Australia. Here summer's approach brings equatorial thunderstorms and rain in superabundance. With the coming of winter, the rains disappear and dry tropical conditions prevail. During the dry season trees may shed their leaves just as their cousins do in the colder winters of the temperate zones. The inverse of the tropical monsoon is the so-called Mediterranean climate, wet and mild in winter, dry and warm in summer. Mediterranean climates, though named because the northern shores of the Mediterranean Sea afford a prime example, are by no means confined to that part of the world. In addition to prevailing in Italy, Spain, Greece, the Balkans, Turkey, and Palestine, Mediterranean climates are found in southwest Africa, central Chile, and southern California.

The contrasting nature of land and sea further modifies the climatic behavior of coastal areas. Because the sea presents a relatively smooth watery plain having a tremendous heat-holding capacity, it warms slowly and cools slowly. Never is its temperature extreme, ranging throughout the world between moderately warm and just freezing. The primary inhomogeneities to be found in the sea are due to the vast currents that slowly move within its depths. These carry tropic waters even into the Arctic and return to equatorial zones with traces of arctic cold still within them. Land, on the other hand, may be mountainous, covered with dense vegetation, barren, flat, or rocky, and hence subject to rapid weather changes.

Coastal-area climates are especially influenced by the sea where the prevailing winds blow inward over the land. Our own west coast and western Europe have climates tending to be marine in nature. They are thus subject to lesser extremes of temperature, because of the prevailing westerly winds. East coasts, like the China coast and our eastern seaboard, have climates more like their respective continental interiors. Their days are warm, their nights are cool. Summers are hot while winters are cold. Where ocean currents sweep past a shore, climates can be so altered as to mask almost completely the geographic location of the land. Warm currents pouring northward from tropic areas of the Atlantic and Pacific give the coasts of Norway and Alaska essentially temperate climates, even though both are in arctic latitudes. Our northwest coast as far south as central California is cooled by ocean currents moving southward from the Arctic.

Mountains and high plateaus too have climates distinctly different from lower terrain in the same geographic location. Increase of precipitation with elevation, clear distinction between the windward and leeward sides of the mountain range, and decrease in the air's density and temperature are the chief characteristics of mountain climates. Precipitation is usually high on the windward side of mountain ranges. Even in normally dry country, vegetation crowns the tops of mountains unless they are so high as to be perpetually covered with snow. When a mountain range fronts the sea its precipitation is especially heavy, often two hundred inches a year. Mountain slopes in Hawaii are soaked with as much as four hundred inches annually. Precipitation increases generally with elevation up to the seven- or eight-thousand-foot level, though the increase is smaller near the Poles than at the equator. Leeward mountain slopes are much drier, even arid or desert, the Gobi Desert in the "rain shadow" of the high Himalaya Mountains being an example. Strong sunlight due to the thinner air, and the bracing quality of the cool, brisk winds, give many mountain districts very enjoyable climates. Though winds of great velocity are often encountered on mountains, the decrease of the air's density partially counterbalances the force that the wind exerts.

Due to the time limitation on our experience, it is natural to assume that climates do not change. Nothing could be more untrue. Over the centuries climatic aberration has been just as erratic as temperate-zone weather is today. For at least nine-tenths of the time back into which geological history reaches, the earth's average temperature has been considerably higher than it is presently and extremes of temperature have been less. Between epochs of roughly 250 million years in which almost the entire earth had a tropical climate there have been cold periods—periods of ice and severe glaciation—lasting a few million years. In addition, there have been numerous smaller fluctuations of climate. Particularly in relatively recent times, we can recognize an entire spectrum of cyclical fluctuations as continually in progress, cycles of small magnitude and short time superimposed on those of greater degree and extent.

Remains of tropical vegetation have been found near both the earth's poles. Both regions have coal deposits which, as far as we know, could only have come from extensive forests. The Sahara was not always dry. Even as glaciers were intruding upon northern Europe some ten thousand years ago, a plateau about nine hundred miles southeast of Algiers, in what is today a dry, almost uninhabited desert, supported a vigorous though primitive population. Judging by thousands of colored drawings to be found in the area's caves, it must have been then a fertile, well-watered land. Debris entrapped in English peat beds during the same period reveals that region to have been largely open tundra with scattered patches of silver birch trees. After 8000 B.C. the English climate, as well as the entire hemisphere, began to grow warmer. Remains of warmth-demanding plants such as oak and elm trees are found in deposits of this period in England. As the glacial ice farther north melted, the level of the oceans rose, a fact clearly demonstrated by salt water flowing over more and more of the peat beds. By 5000 B.C. England became separated from the Continent, and since that time a climate about like its present-day one has ensued. This particular warming cycle reached its crest about 3000 B.C., at which time world conditions were a few degrees warmer than now.

From 3000 B.C. to sometime between 1600 and 1900 A.D. the world thus underwent a general cooling. Glacial evidence, radio-carbon dating (see Chapter 3), and deposits of pollen and other sediment reveal to scientists versed in such matters that cycles of smaller amplitude were superimposed on this general reduction in temperature. From 500 B.C. to 100 A.D. conditions were somewhat cooler and wetter; from 400 to 1000 A.D. they were warmer and drier; and from about 1300 A.D. to modern times they were again cooler and wetter.

Written weather records of ancient times are scarce, but a few stretch back quite a number of centuries. A second-century geog-rapher, Claudius Ptolemaeus of Alexandria, kept a diary of Egyp-tian weather. Having no thermometer or rain gauge, he could record only thunderstorms, rainy days, the wind and its direction, but this alone indicates a striking contrast when compared with today. Then rain was almost as common in summer as in winter; now summers are rainless. Thunderstorms were frequent in the hot season, while now they are unknown. Then summer winds alter-nated from the north, south, and west; now prevailing summer winds are from the north.

Other indirect evidence of climatic change is shown by ancient Japanese records. The dates on which the cherry trees blossomed in the old Japanese capital of Kyoto were faithfully noted by govern-ment historians as far back as 800 A.D., it being the custom for the Emperor to hold a festival each year beneath the trees in full bloom. This record, indicating an early or late spring, gives an integrated picture of temperature that tells more than could vol-umes of day-to-day measurements. It shows a long period extending from the eleventh to the fourteenth century which was decidedly colder than the average. Somewhat the same story is afforded by the saga of a Norse culture that was flourishing in Greenland in the eleventh century A.D., yet by the fourteenth century had ceased to exist. Though climate probably was not the sole cause of this colony's bad times, archeologists have irrefutable evidence of its considerable change in Greenland. For one thing, ancient graves with tree roots intertwined among the bones have been found in the southern part of the island where now the ground is permanently frozen.

The climatic history of western North America back hundreds of years is revealed through the concentric rings some long-lived tree trunks show by virtue of their annual growth cycle. Wide spacing between the rings represents a year of considerable rain and much growth; narrow separation means little rainfall and little growth. The most pronounced climatic fluctuation revealed by dendrochronologic data is a two-hundred-year oscillation during the thirteenth and fourteenth centuries. From 1215 A.D. to the end of that century, rainfall far below normal seems to have been the rule in the Colorado River basin. In agreement, archeological evidence shows that prolonged droughts during this time drove southwestern Pueblo Indians from the area. But about 1300 A.D. wetter weather set in, and it continued for some ninety years before returning to more normal, drier times. A peculiar rainfall-pattern change about the mid-1600's is also indicated. Before this time a tendency to long-time cycles of wet and dry prevailed in the southern California region, but after it the cycles became much shorter in duration. The reverse is shown in the Missouri River basin; short-time variations were more common there preceding 1650 A.D.

Coming down to modern times a pattern of climatic change persists, though detailed records go back only about a hundred years for a few localities and some sixty years for this nation as a whole. Such a short period of time does not show what some might consider a very impressive change, but small changes have very significant consequences nonetheless. A 1-degree shift in mean annual temperature is equivalent to roughly a hundred miles of latitude; one degree is the difference between the climates of Baltimore and Philadelphia. An 8- to 10-degree drop in the world's temperature would be enough to permit a gradual accumulation of ice and snow year after year until much of the North American continent as well as Europe and Asia would eventually disappear under sheets of ice, as they did some twenty thousand years ago. A 5-degree rise, if maintained a few thousand years, would surely melt some of the six million square miles of ice and snow now collected at the Poles, thereby raising the levels of the oceans throughout the world. Such an increase would very likely bring tropical conditions to most of the earth. Carried far enough—though no one knows precisely what this might be, 10 degrees is a reasonable guess—to melt all of the gigantic ice sheets at the South Pole, ocean levels would rise a couple of hundred feet, for these sheets are as much as two miles thick. In such an event coast lines would change enormously; ocean currents would shift as a consequence, and the whole pattern of climate as we now know it would be altered. Lest anyone become apprehensive that in the near future London will disappear beneath the ocean, or that steaming jungles will overrun Chicago, he can take heart from the fact that nature would require at least five thousand years to bring about sufficient climatic change to alter drastically our way of life.

During the last century temperatures have risen in the Northern Hemisphere as a whole somewhere between 1 and 2 degrees Fahrenheit. Southern Hemisphere data are scanty, but a similar warming in its middle and lower latitudes is indicated; the Antarctic too is growing warmer. Measurements at Little America show that the last fifty years have seen an average temperature rise of about five degrees. Moreover, recent studies made in a 1000-foot shaft cut into the Antarctic ice suggest that the warming began at least ten centuries ago. The general change has been in the form of milder winters, with the colder areas receiving the most increase and warm areas being less affected. Spitsbergen and eastern Greenland have in recent years experienced average winter temperatures between 6 and 13 degrees warmer than they were at the turn of the century. Spitsbergen's harbor used to be icebound from October through June; now it is open seven months a year. The growing season in Finland has increased some twenty days during the last hundred years. Lakes in northern Russia freeze seven days later and break up an average of five days earlier. Subzero temperatures are only half as common now in Montreal as they were in the late 1800's;

the snowfall, which averaged 130 inches in the 1880's, has in recent years reached only about 80 inches. With only a few exceptions, glaciers from the Alps to Alaska have been shrinking. Some hotels built in Switzerland at the turn of the century to front upon scenic wonderlands of ice now do not even have glaciers in view. The Thames and Tiber rivers, once habitually ice-covered in winter, have not frozen over for years.

In our northeastern and north central states, average winter temperatures have climbed 3.5 degrees during the last sixty years. Southern winter temperatures rose a little more than 2.5 degrees in the period 1894 to 1954, southwestern ones by an average of 1 degree. Summer temperature trends, in contrast, are up everywhere by less than 1 degree except in our north central states, where the increase seems to have been a little more than 1 degree. Tropical and subtropical zones have become, if anything, a little cooler in the last half-century.

That the Northern Hemisphere has been warming is shown most dramatically by its fauna and flora. Birds, justly famous for reading weather signs, have shifted northward. The cardinal, tufted titmouse, mockingbird, and hooded warbler, once regarded as southern habitants, have been found in recent years in the north central states and even in New England. Species that used to migrate south with the winter now stay north throughout the year. Northern Europe is being invaded by Mediterranean birds. Fifty years ago the opossum was rarely seen north of Virginia; now opossums are common as far north as Boston. Deer, moose, racoons, and badgers are moving north also. Even fish are migrating; whiting, king mackerel, halibut, and haddock range farther north than they have ever been known to do before. The cod, once unknown in Greenland, is currently a food staple of the Eskimos.

Larch, spruce, yellow birch, sugar maple, black ash, and white pine, trees that demand cold weather, have been growing farther north also. Our Midwestern corn belt extends five hundred miles farther north; wheat cultivation has advanced some two or three hundred miles into Canada. Once-frozen Russian steppes that never knew a plow have been brought into production in recent years. Scandinavian mountainsides that were covered with ice for centuries are presently being plowed; forests also have been inching up the mountain slopes.

With our present knowledge, or rather lack of it, it would be imprudent to make extrapolations of the consequences of a continued temperature rise. It will be remembered that, with the possible exception of the last sixty-odd years, temperatures have been decreasing slowly since about 3000 B.C. This latest cycle may very well be a minor one too; in fact, a downward trend may already be in the making. In the United States, recorded temperatures averaged over all the seasons reached a peak in 1939, and have since that time been falling at about the same rate that they climbed in the previous forty-five years. Winter-month temperatures reached a peak in 1935, at which point they showed a rise of 1.9 degrees above 1894. For sixty years since 1894, the entire wintertime uptrend stands at only 1.5 degrees. Thus, on a nation-wide basis, winters have become colder since 1935. Confirmation of this latest trend may be indicated by the story of our northwestern glaciers. In Waterton Glacier International Park along the United States-Canadian border, during the first half of this century several of the largest glaciers completely disappeared, while others shrank anywhere from 60 to 75 per cent. For a while it looked as if all the glaciers would disappear, but since 1950 they have held their own and park personnel have ceased to worry about them. Glaciers on Mount Rainier and Mount Baker likewise have been advancing and thickening since 1949.

If we knew precisely what caused climatic fluctuations, we might be in a better position to forecast whether a warmer, colder, wetter, or drier period was ahead. Present theories of why climates change involve elevation or depression of the continents, wobble in the earth's spin on its axis, the eccentricity of the earth's orbit, differences in the amount of dust in the air, shifts in ocean currents, solar variation, and changes in the quantity of carbon dioxide in the atmosphere. While it is entirely possible that each of these factors has influenced the earth's climate at particular times and places, the problem of world-wide climatic change is yet very much like a mystery drama in which each suspect has some kind of alibi.

The main objection to ideas involving an alteration of our planet's topography is that we have apparently had large climatic changes in the last several thousand years in regions where geological conditions have been stable. Wobble of the earth as a climatic factor does not agree with indications that major climate changes have occurred in both hemispheres simultaneously, not alternately. Dust haze has been observed to cut out an appreciable fraction of the sun's incoming energy for periods of several years, as after Krakatoa's eruption, but few believe volcanic upheavals can account for more than transitory changes—that is, for some of the minor cycles.

The eccentricity of the earth's orbit causes there to be a considerable variation in the rate at which radiation is received from the sun but the change in the yearly radiation income is insignificant. Accordingly this factor meets with difficulty as an explanation of world-wide shifts in climate. The effect is not without climatic consequences nevertheless. Presently the earth swings closest to the sun in January and farthest in July, making seasonal changes milder in the Northern Hemisphere and more severe in the Southern. In 10,000 years the phases will shift so that the reverse will be true and Northern Hemisphere summers will be hotter and the winters colder. Then in about 21,000 years we will be back to January for the closest approach again.

The ocean-current theory, recently revived because of new analyses of ocean-floor deposits taken from depths up to nearly five miles, ascribes the advance and retreat of glaciers, hence so-called ice ages, to the interchange of water between the Atlantic and Arctic oceans. With free circulation, the theory says the Arctic Ocean stays unfrozen thanks to the warmer Atlantic currents, but because it is unfrozen more water evaporates, greater snows fall, and glaciers grow on northern lands. Eventually so much water accumulates in the glaciers that ocean levels fall, unrestricted flow between the oceans ceases, and the Arctic Ocean freezes over. With this source of moisture now cut off, less snow is produced, and the glaciers slowly diminish. The water released replenishes the oceans, and circulation is again established until the cycle starts all over again. If oceanographers read the signs correctly, the Arctic Ocean last froze over only 11,000 years ago, and the world today is heading for another invasion of glacial ice. Although this timetable fits in neatly with migrations of Indians across our continent and the habitation of areas in the Sahara, the theory must still stand the scrutiny of other scientific disciplines.

The sun, being the prime source of all our weather as well as climate, has long been suspected of having a hand in climate changes; but accusations of it have been framed with caution, largely because measurements of solar heat made daily for more than forty years by the Smithsonian Institution of Washington, D.C., have not disclosed significant trends in the solar energy reaching the earth. Recently, however, indications of solar variability not involving the over-all heat output of the sun have reopened the question of the sun's role. Outbursts of ultraviolet and corpuscular energy such as accompany sunspots account for only a few per cent of the sun's total energy; precisely how much is unknown, since virtually all of it is stopped high in the earth's upper atmosphere, where it causes long-range radio-communications interruption and vivid auroral displays. The first definite knowledge that corpuscles also produce great upper-air heating was radioed to earth from high-altitude weather balloons released from Berlin in February, 1952. Coinciding with a severe solar disturbance, the air at altitudes of 90,000 to 100,000 feet jumped from a minus 76 to about zero degrees Fahrenheit, the warmest ever known for air at that height. Soon thereafter there occurred a striking reversal in the air's circulation over polar regions, violent storms developed over the Atlantic, and record snows fell. On February 11, 1958, our satellite Explorer I signaled a sharp rise in cosmic ray activity, presumably resulting from a large solar storm. Three days later intense cold and heavy snows descended on the eastern half of the

United States, leading some meteorologists to conclude that the succession of events was more than a mere coincidence. Though much observation and research remain to be done before a working theory is developed from such incidents, the sun may yet be found to be a main force behind climatic change.

The carbon-dioxide theory is likewise of much current interest, and is in a similar position in that only time and research can resolve its validity. When trees are chopped down, when once-rural land is bulldozed for new suburbs, when factories and refineries are built on open fields, it is readily apparent that the amount of carbon dioxide taken from the air by growing plants is decreased while the amount added through fuel consumption is increased. This net yearly addition of carbon dioxide now amounts to something like six billion tons—enough, according to calculations, to cause an increase in the earth's temperature of 1.5 degrees in a century. If industrialization at the present rate is continued, the theory would further suggest that by the year 2080 temperatures might be up 4 degrees, other possible changes being disregarded.

In simplest terms, carbon dioxide could work this change through a kind of greenhouse effect. Like the glass panes of such a structure, carbon dioxide throughout the atmosphere imposes a one-way street on some of the sun's incoming energy. The gas is almost completely transparent to the radiations of a hot, glowing body such as the sun but partially opaque to those of a cooler mass like the earth, and thus it hinders heat's escape from the earth. Just how effective a warden carbon dioxide might be is now unknown, but its considerable variation in the atmosphere would seem to have climatic consequences.

Whether carbon dioxide, dust, the sun, or an agent yet unidentified is ultimately established as the principal regulator of climate, there can be no doubt that man himself has had a hand in climate changes. Overgrazed land retains less moisture than that with grass cover, cut woodland less than forest, and pavement none at all. Plowing permits both wind and rain to carry away alluvial soil in which might have grown erosion-preventing plants. When dry spells come, ill-treated lands that tend to be arid at best have a small margin of safety and bit by bit deserts take over. This very thing has been happening in the Midwestern United States in recent years. Canada and Venezuela have seen similar trouble coming. Some South African areas have already been ruined almost beyond repair, while the damage in China and parts of the southern and eastern Mediterranean littoral was done thousands of years ago. Ancient Babylon, having a magnificent imperial palace, priceless art treasures, and the famous Hanging Gardens, was in a fertile region and at the height of its glory was called the "granary of the world." Somewhere nearby was reputed to have been the Garden of Eden. Extensive forests of cedars spread across the land. Indeed, the whole area was undoubtedly rich, green, and productive. Now only a few remnants of the famous cedar forests remain in Lebanon, and winds off the Persian Gulf and every other wind that blows merely shift the dry sands. Reckless, ignorant ravage of the land, the result of cutting trees and of overgrazing, is largely responsible. Whether such regions will be reclaimed from the desert remains to be seen. That they could be—given enough time, effort, and money —is certain.

Climate, of course, has a profound effect on all living things, but the extent to which climates and climatic changes are responsible for our variety of species, our racial characteristics, and our civilization is not so obvious. As our climate has grown increasingly variable, plant and animal forms also have become increasingly capable of adaptation. Having to respond to changing conditions has caused plants to become more hardy and animals more intelligent. The great majority of animal species are now sufficiently adaptable to range far and wide. The puma lives anywhere between Patagonia and Canada, the raven from the Sahara to Greenland, and the toad from Morocco to Norway. Creatures that could not adapt, the dinosaur for instance, were dropped by the wayside. Man, of course, is the most adaptable and presumably the most intelligent being yet to inhabit the earth.

Body size in warm-blooded animals having an extensive geographical range is closely related to climate, larger size being characteristic of colder climates. The reason is simply one of geometry. The larger a body, shape being identical, the smaller is the ratio of skin area to bulk, the area varying as the square while bulk varies as the cube. The larger the animal, therefore, the less food, proportionally, it must consume to maintain body temperatures. A small mammal such as a mouse is in constant danger of becoming too cold; it must eat considerably more than its own weight daily to compensate for its relatively large heat-radiating surface. Human beings, where they have stayed in one location for some time, conform to the geometric rule. In Europe the Finns have a mean weight of 154 pounds, while up the temperature scale the Spaniards weigh 132 pounds and the Berbers of Algeria only 124 pounds. In Asia, Mongoloid peoples show a similar scaling from the North Chinese at 142 pounds to the Annamites at 112 pounds. Lowest sizes go with equatorial tribes like the Bushmen of the Kalahari, among whom even the male population averages only 89 pounds.

Plants likewise show the results of climate change, but more noticeably they show a remarkable degree of adaptation to a specific atmospheric environment. Subtle changes so unobtrusive as only recently to have come to light are involved. Tomato plants, for example, will not produce unless they get a daily fluctuation of temperature. Daytime temperatures of 79 degrees Fahrenheit and nighttime ones of 64 are nearly perfect for this particular plant. Why tomato production is usually low in the tropics even though the plants themselves may grow profusely, and why some years are better than others, is thus explained. The potato plant likewise produces best when the nighttime temperature drops, in this case to between 50 and 57 degrees. Accordingly, it is suited to the climate of Maine, Idaho, and Ireland. Other plants show similar responses, though to varying extents. Some need different optimal temperatures for each stage of growth—formation of the stalk, flowering, and seeding. Many deciduous trees require a definite period of cold for fruit production when spring arrives. Some plants are sensitive to the time sequence of day and night; others, as we have seen, respond to a cycle of dry and rainy seasons.

That climate has had a considerable effect and still exerts an influence upon the course of civilizations is unquestioned. Obviously man can thrive best in a climate where his major efforts need not be directed solely toward survival. With a few exceptions, earliest civilizations of which we have records seem to have developed along a line where the present average temperature is close to 70 degrees and which then could have differed only a very few degrees. The early Peruvian culture flowered at a somewhat lower average temperature, but the region's high elevation and the unusually bright sunlight could have been compensating factors. The Mayan civilization developed in a region that is now warmer, but here there is evidence of significant climatic changes within historic times.

Only after the discovery and use of fire to create a "private environment" did civilization spread northward. Migrations to the northern shores of the Mediterranean, northern China, and India are directly linked to this discovery. At the present time the most energetic nations—on the basis of world trade, national income, military power, political influence, and such—group about a 60-degree temperature line. Some geographers, seeing in this a need for a certain amount of cold to stimulate the best efforts of men, prophesy a further northward shift of centers of world influence. They maintain that as mastery of the thermal environment increases, the adequacy of cold temperatures to evoke the necessary stimulus will diminish and more vigorous peoples will be inclined to move still farther north. They overlook two factors: with the coming of air-conditioning a new dimension is added to man's control of his environment, and the idea that hot climates make for lassitude has been overemphasized.

By all scientific criteria men are tropical animals. They are not like cattle, for example, which do not sweat well and must rest during the hot part of the day even in temperate zones to avoid overheating; men are born with sweat glands and can work safely in the heat. That the tropics are no place for a white man and that a black man is better suited to hot climates are simply myths. It is equally false that white man must not expose himself to the deadly rays of the equatorial sun and that hot climates are intrinsically debilitating. This idea, which is so prevalent today, arose from the European's custom for reasons of prestige and modesty of appearing fully clothed at all times, including helmet with spine pad, even in the tropics. Under such encumbrances a man naturally overheats, and as a result his energy and endurance wane. World War II investigations especially went far toward dispelling this doctrine. With a short period of acclimatization and a minimum of clothing to permit evaporative cooling, a white man can keep pace with any African native. Furthermore, by sweating he will feel relatively cool. In reality, then, populations in the future are likely to spread both northward and southward, for there is no climate in which, with knowledge and modern technology, man cannot thrive.

13 a ravaged realm

> . . . *this most excellent canopy, the air, look you, this brave o'erhanging firmament, this majestical roof fretted with golden fire—why, it appears no other thing to me than a foul and pestilent congregation of vapours.*
>
> SHAKESPEARE

THE AVERAGE person daily eats two and three-quarters pounds of food, drinks four and one-half pounds of water, but breathes about twenty pounds of air. He can refuse to eat suspected food or to drink water of doubtful purity, but he must breathe such air as is available, even though it may be contaminated and a danger to health and even to life itself. Unfortunately, modern industrialized society has forced nearly half the population of America and equally large segments of the peoples of other countries to live or work in environments polluted to some degree with smoke, dust, and chemical fumes from factories, processing plants, heating units, incinerators, and automobile exhausts. Air pollution has thus become a social evil of widespread consequences, but it may be only a prelude to something far more disastrous. Air-borne contaminants produced by atomic and nuclear weapons are capable of blanketing the earth in the space of an hour with a deadly cloud, and enormous stocks of never-before-used war gases and bacterial agents exist which could be the parents of wave after wave of disease and death. It is high time for peoples everywhere to realize that we all live in the same ocean of air, that we draw sustenance from it, and that, if we violate the air beyond a limit, complete and irrevocable destruction will be our reward.

Pure air, if defined as that containing its usual chemical components in their customary proportions, is now approached only on mountain tops and at mid-ocean. Even there the same atmosphere to which man has adapted himself through many generations is not to be found since the dawn of the atomic age. To be sure, what might be considered normal air has been polluted to some degree since the beginning of time and will never be pure in the future. As described in previous chapters, dusts and vapors are given off by volcanoes. Smoke in tremendous quantities is produced by forest and grass fires. Sand and soil from desert or drought regions are spread over large areas by the winds. Air-borne pollens and other allergens derived from plants seasonally reach great proportions. To these man has now added the miasma arising from his own activities, our "sin of emission," as air pollution has been called. Smoke, soot, and the smell of the stockyards, though annoying, are mere tokens of more noxious emanations; real difficulties develop, we have learned, when traces of gases unite under the influence of sunlight or when meteorological conditions favor accumulation of gaseous emissions instead of dissipation.

The world was first made aware that large segments of the atmosphere could be unintentionally poisoned with "aerial garbage" by an extraordinary event that occurred in the Meuse River valley of Belgium in 1930. Following three days of heavy fog generously mixed with smoke from nearby Liége factory chimneys, the populace of the neat little farms spread along the river awoke coughing, to find their livestock choking and writhing in agony on the ground. Two nightmarish days and nights followed. Some families barricaded themselves indoors with as many of their animals as remained by stuffing wet rags in every crack. Others, like the three thousand inhabitants of Engis, left in panic-stricken flight. Even so, sixty-three persons and a great many animals died, while hundreds of persons were left gasping with throats and chests feeling as if they had been seared with flame.

The cause was neither the Black Death—the scourge of fourteenth-century Europe—nor uncovered German gas supplies left from World War I, as many thought at the time. The precise agent responsible probably will never be known because tests were not made until some time afterward. It may have been fluorine compounds released by phosphate works, sulfur dioxide from the high-sulphur-content coal being burned in the Liége area, or both. Most authorities blame the latter, for, along with black clouds of smoke, tons of this gas were being released daily into the air. At the time of the tragedy, a meteorological condition called an inversion—warm air on top of cold air—settled down upon the hills surrounding the Meuse and effectively put a roof over the valley. The trapped sulfur dioxide first reacted with the oxygen of the air to form sulfur trioxide, which in turn combined with the moisture in the air to become sulfuric acid. This sulfuric acid, collecting in tiny fog droplets and about smoke and soot particles, caused acute irritation of the lungs and throats of the victims, which resulted eventually in vomiting and death through heart failure.

This tragic incident, although arousing world-wide interest at the time, was soon forgotten, and similar events were destined to occur again. *Collier's Magazine* carried a prophetic warning in the issue of October 23, 1948, that it could happen here. It did, and soon. During the last week of October, 1948, a condition of smoke and fog—by now called a smog—settled down about the town of Donora, Pennsylvania [Plate 7]. At first no unusual significance was attached to it, for short-duration smogs were not uncommon in this industrial town of fourteen thousand nestled beside the Monongahela River. By Wednesday morning, October 27, visibility was poor and the smog was a subject of conversation. It continued throughout Thursday, and by Friday morning half of the people of

Donora were coughing. But since it was late fall and the season for colds, few realized that anything dreadful was imminent. During Friday a marked increase in illnesses became obvious. That evening the doctors' telephone lines were jammed with calls. The fire department, the American Red Cross chapter, and other local organizations were called on for aid. The first death came about two o'clock Saturday morning. Other deaths followed in quick succession during the day, and before midnight seventeen persons had died. Two more deaths occurred on Sunday and another, attributed to consequences of the smog, a week later. Altogether, twenty persons died from the polluted air, and nearly half of the area's inhabitants were sickened. Fourteen hundred and forty persons were officially listed as seriously ill; some of them were still disabled a year later. In addition, hundreds of domestic animals—pets in Donora and livestock and chickens in the surrounding countryside—perished.

As in the Meuse Valley incident, Donora's plight arose during a weather condition that was unique both in severity and duration. Whereas before, pollutants had been dissipated satisfactorily by the normal air circulation, a temperature inversion accompanied by an extraordinarily slow air movement permitted contaminants to accumulate for more than four days. The evidence points again to sulfur dioxide, produced in the grates of many coal fires for home heating as well as in the furnaces of nearby industries.

In 1952 the most spectacular case of atmospheric poisoning yet hit London, a city that has had a long history of air pollution. King Edward I found it necessary to issue a proclamation (circa 1300) prohibiting the use of "sea coales," as coal was then called, within London. Though a craftsman was tried, condemned, and executed in 1306 for this offense, the order was gradually relaxed, and by the time of Queen Elizabeth I the prohibition was in effect only during sessions of Parliament, even though it is recorded that the Queen "findeth hersealfe greatly grieved and annoyed by the taste and smoake of the sea coales." Still later, in 1661, the diarist and public servant John Evelyn published an illuminating protest in which he referred to impure mist and filthy vapor, saying that "catharrs, phthisicks, coughs and consumptions rage more in this one city than in the whole earth besides." Despite this and innumerable black fogs in other years, London was hardly prepared for the great fog.

On Thursday afternoon, December 4, a fog began like many another English fog. By Friday morning one could just see his own feet. Groping along the sidewalk, one might catch glimpses of faces without bodies gliding past. Traffic moved convoy-fashion—with someone walking ahead calling directions to the drivers. As the day wore on and smoke from a daily consumption of seventy thousand tons of coal poured from millions of dwelling and factory chimneys, the color of the fog changed from a dirty white to brown, then black, and everyone began to cough. Weather forecasters could report no relief in sight, for there was neither wind nor promise of any, and the air aloft was not cooler, but warmer, than the fog layer choking the city. In short, London's situation was identical to what had previously befallen the Meuse Valley and Donora.

During Saturday conditions became critical for many individuals. Persons with a tendency to bronchitis or asthma gasped for breath as their lungs burned and their hearts labored. Doctors, finding themselves with far more patients than they could have visited even with normal traffic conditions, resorted to the telephone, though about all they could suggest was to get in an oxygen tent if possible. By Sunday morning visibility was down to an incredible eleven inches; literally, one could not see his hand in front of his face. People along the docks, being unable to see, walked off into the water and were drowned. Others, becoming lost, sat down in despair only to die of exposure.

On Monday the smog rose a bit, settled down again, then disappeared, and London began the grim task of counting the cost. Though the normal death rate for London at the time was slightly under 2000 per week, deaths during the week of the smog were 4703 and the next week 3138, a greater increase above the expected normal than occurred during the worst week of the 1886 London cholera epidemic. Altogether, medical statisticians calculated the smog was responsible for at least four thousand deaths. In addition, the city was encrusted with dirt and soot. Furniture and walls were covered with a slimy black film. Curtains and clothing often disintegrated while being cleaned.

True to the patterns in other cases of heavy pollution, the London smog hit hardest the very young, the old, and those suffering from chronic respiratory or heart disorders. Ninety per cent of those who died were over forty-five years of age, and nearly 70 per cent were over sixty-five. The great majority of healthy individuals found the smog little more than a temporary nuisance. But those who conclude from this that atmospheric pollution is largely "a violation of man's aesthetic sensibilities" could not be more wrong. Polluted air attacks our clothing, our skin, our lungs. It causes metals to corrode, paint to flake, vegetation to become stunted and blackened. It shuts out cleansing sunlight, permitting germs to multiply and our natural disease resistance to be lowered. In short, air contamination reduces our vitality in innumerable ways.

Compared to the hundred trillion tons of air overlying America, our estimated yearly outpouring of fifty million tons of aerial waste does not seem much. It is, in fact, only one-half part contamination in one million parts of pure air. But with the connivance of the weather, lethal concentrations could be quickly reached in a great many localities. Human beings cannot long tolerate carbon monoxide if it exceeds one hundred parts per million; chlorine, one part per million; fluorine, three parts per million; nitrogen oxides, twenty-five parts per million; sulfur dioxide, ten parts per million; ozone, one part per million; and so on. Formaldehyde irritates the eyes when it reaches one part per million. Hydrogen fluoride in a concentration of only one-half part per million parts of air damages some plants in a few hours. When dust and smoke particles occur mixed with these gases, even lower concentrations become dangerous because the gases tend to congregate about the particles, making the former much more likely to be retained in the respiratory system.

Even though concentrations of pollutants sufficient to kill rather large numbers of people rapidly have occurred in only a few instances, impressive evidence comes from many sources that slowly, insidiously, air pollution is reaping a frightful toll. In fact, the world has a new and rising epidemic on its hands. In the last twenty years diagnosed cases of lung cancer have increased 400 per cent. The smoking habit, so widely blamed for the increase, is undoubtedly a contributing factor, for tobacco smoke cannot be regarded as other than as an extreme case of air pollution. But it is certainly not the only cause, perhaps not even the major one. Lung cancer is most prevalent in cities and industrial areas, and it began to increase before cigarette-smoking became as common as it is now. Some pollution sleuths, notably in Britain, have found a geographic correlation between lung-cancer incidence and the number of chimneys per acre; others, in this country, between its prevalence and the amount of time spent in motor traffic. Such correlations, though they may seem farfetched at first, are not unrealistic. Scientists from the United States Public Health Service and its National Cancer Institute have extracted compounds from the air of major cities and found them, even in minute doses, capable of causing cancer in laboratory animals. In fact, one of the most potent carcinogenic substances known, benzopyrene, is found in the air over many cities of the world.

The link between air pollution and lung cancer is particularly enlightening. The father-daughter team of Dr. Clarence A. Mills and Dr. Marjorie Mills Porter of Cincinnati found cigarette smoke, automobile exhaust fumes, and industrial pollution all potent cancer causes. Cigarette-smoking alone, they determined, increases the chances of lung cancer from four to twenty times, depending on the amount smoked. Driving twelve thousand or more miles a year in heavy traffic exposes one to exhaust fumes that multiply the risk of lung cancer by another two or three times. The rate is doubled again for those who live in polluted downtown areas. A heavy-smoking cab-driver whose residence is in a polluted section is thus exposed to all three dangers, and he is 120 times more likely to develop lung cancer than a nonsmoking farmer.

Cancer is not the only result; respiratory diseases are definitely tied to atmospheric pollution. Pneumonia and tuberculosis claim the lives of several times as many men in the dirty districts of Chicago as in the cleaner suburbs. It is calculated that in this one city some seven hundred more persons die each year as a result of pollution than would be expected if the death rate of suburban areas prevailed over the whole city. Another case in point is an illness labeled "Yokohama asthma" by American soldiers, though the sickness is prevalent not only in Yokohama but also in many other port cities that, like Yokohama, are ringed by hills and have varied industries fouling the air. Here during the fall and winter persistent colds are common to Westerners as well as to the Japanese. Exertion causes a sufferer to gasp for breath and to wake in the wee hours of the morning with a suffocating feeling. Year after year each case gets worse, sometimes becoming uncontrollable, with the patient bordering on collapse. So far, the only treatment for Yokohama asthma is to leave Yokohama. Los Angeles, a city noted for its salubrious climate, was until recent years a favorable site for tuberculosis sanitariums. Now the Los Angeles smog constitutes a definite health hazard and the sanitariums are closing. Germs multiply when cleansing sunlight is shut out.

Farm animals are poisoned even more readily than man by deleterious atmospheres. Cattle not only face the hazard of inhaling polluted air, but they ingest contaminated vegetation. While the permissible inhaling limit for a man over an eight-hour period is three parts of a fluoride per million of air, cattle-poisoning may develop where the concentration reaches only a few parts per billion, or less, because of an accumulation of the contaminant on the cattle's forage. Instances of animal-poisoning thus occur rather frequently in the vicinity of brick kilns, aluminum and phosphate fertilizer plants, and steel mills.

Vegetation is itself a sensitive indicator of air-fouling, and reveals very clearly the increasing rate at which our air is being plundered. Prior to 1948, any vegetable could be grown in the vicinity of Los Angeles. Now many cannot be grown locally; in fact, plant damage extends some fifty miles from the city's center. Damage around other metropolitan areas—New York, San Francisco, Baltimore, Philadelphia, London, Paris, Copenhagen, São Paulo, Bogotá—extends up to fifteen miles. Dr. Frits W. Went, former California Institute of Technology plant physiologist (now Director of the Missouri Botanical Garden), has pointed out a considerable parallel between the prevalence of plant damage and gasoline usage. Roughly, he finds that when consumption reaches twelve tons per square mile per day, symptoms, such as a silvering of the lower surfaces of tender leaves and stunted growth, appear.

The economic costs of air pollution are exorbitant, though a definite price tag is impossible to determine for the simple reason that the very nature of the losses from contaminated air cannot be separated from those from other causes. Nearly a decade ago the United States Geological Survey reported that smoke damage to merchandise and buildings alone reached a half-billion dollars a year in this country. A 1949 estimate places the direct annual cost of air pollution at one and one-half billion dollars; a 1958 report raised it to four billion. The material loss just in New York in fabrics, household items, and buildings has been placed at $100,-000,000 annually. An estimate for Chicago, based on excessive laundry bills, injuries to fabrics, buildings, metal products, and the loss of heating efficiency, puts the yearly figure for that city at $50,000,000. Other independent estimates have placed the damage for Pittsburgh at $10,000,000, Cincinnati at $8,000,000, and Cleveland at $6,000,000. Indicative of the terrific total cost, large hotels, department stores, and hospitals rate their individual annual losses due to atmospheric pollution from $4000 to $50,000. In Britain the yearly cost is put at £250,000,000.

Airlines lose thousands of dollars each month in canceled flights because of smog. Innumerable automobile accidents occur because of poor visibility, again due to smog. Iron rusts something like three times as fast in heavily industrialized cities as it does in other towns; furthermore, all common metal objects corrode more rapidly in towns than in the country. Wood, cotton, leather, and other materials derived from growing matter decay more rapidly in polluted atmospheres as a result of acid attack. Sandstones, lime-stones, slates, and mortar also are attacked by the acid constituents of polluted atmospheres. Ultimately the stone disintegrates under-neath the surface and large flakes slip off. Building property in Britain is damaged in this manner to the extent of £2,500,000 a year, according to a 1930 estimate. Moreover, the chemicals re-sponsible for all this damage would themselves have been worth millions of dollars if they could have been recovered. Finally, the behavior of polluted air is in striking contrast to that of normal air with regard to cloud formation and rain initiation, though just what the consequences may be on weather processes is now largely a matter of conjecture.

Atmospheric pollution is the sum of many individual sources. Ironically, the public itself is responsible for much of the polluted air, though it has only a vague concept of its part. A few big smoke-stacks belching smoke visible for miles seem infinitely more im-portant than home chimneys, incinerators, or automobile exhausts. There are hundreds and thousands of the latter, however, for each industrial smokestack. In Donora, for example, the metallurgical plants were blamed for that city's tragic smog, but later when a labor strike stopped all industrial activity, the sulfur dioxide con-tent of the air—the agent considered responsible—dropped barely 25 per cent. London's some two million open fireplaces inefficiently burning soft coal, and not her factories with elaborate furnaces, are the chief cause of her black fogs. After forcing strict regulations on her refineries and factories in recent years, Los Angeles still found holding her own in the smog battle impossible because 65 per cent of the ashes and soot in her air was coming from back-yard rubbish-burning. Automobiles, trucks, and buses, permitting about 7 per cent of the gasoline fed to them to pass unburned, contribute 400,000 gallons of irritants a day. As a result this one source was pouring out approximately one-quarter of the total contaminants in Los Angeles and three-quarters of the petroleum-caused pollution. Now new, very stringent laws are being enacted in a further attempt to solve the old problem. Some 90 per cent of nonautomotive smog sources have been brought under control; the beleaguered city still has its automobiles to contend with, however.

Los Angeles presently rates the dubious distinction of being this nation's severest sufferer from air pollution. Aware that the city has barely missed disaster on several occasions, her public health officials stand ready, should the situation get out of hand, to order the city's refineries shut down, to halt the sale of gasoline, and even to advise the governor of California to declare the city a disaster area under martial law. Though there is an appreciable rise in the illness rate on smoggy days, the most widely noticed effects have been smarting eyes and sore throats. In this respect the Los Angeles situation is not unique; other cities across the country—Chicago, Washington, D.C., New York, Philadelphia, Jacksonville, as well as much of the area from New England to Virginia—have experienced the eye-watering condition that heralds smog troubles [Plate 7]. Honolulu also has begun to experience Los Angeles-type smog.

Detroit, along with Los Angeles, is filling her air with lead fumes from automobile exhausts nearly to the limit of human tolerance at rush hours. The Gulf Coast, experiencing rapid industrialization during recent years, has also encountered air-contamination difficulties. In point of tonnage, the Houston area discharges more chemicals into the air than any other locality in either Canada or the United States. If the surrounding terrain were not generally flat, giving rise to rather constant winds, the entire area would indeed be in a deplorable situation. As it is, house and automobile paint is occasionally damaged, trees and other vegetation are sometimes harmed, and many florists have been forced to move elsewhere. This story could be repeated with small variations for every section of the country; in fact, an estimated ten thousand United States cities have air-pollution problems. Los Angeles, however, provides the most convincing evidence of how an atmospheric malady develops.

Los Angeles is simply the first city to have outgrown her air supply. There, in a basin surrounded on three sides by mountains, now live five million people who drive half that number of automobiles and burn daily fifty thousand tons of fuel, most of it petroleum products. Automobiles, trucks, and buses alone release about four billion cubic feet of exhaust gases each day. Two thousand tons of organic vapors from refineries, chemical plants, dry-cleaning establishments, paint-spraying operations, and the like are released each day. Even the sixty-five million cigarettes smoked daily in Los Angeles county contribute almost twelve tons of contaminants. On the fourth side, almost constant onshore breezes from the Pacific Ocean form a barrier quite as effective as the mountains. Instead of blowing up and over the mountains, the cooler Pacific air is often trapped by overriding hot, dry air off the Mojave Desert—again a temperature inversion. The effect is like putting a lid on a gigantic gas chamber.

Though the Los Angeles ailment is called "smog," the term is a misnomer. Smoke is not a major problem; literally something new under the sun seems to have come to pass. According to latest theories, the vaporous evil that causes most of the smarting eyes and sore throats arises from a combination of faint wisps of chemicals given off wherever fuel is burned in air and unburned petroleum fumes released largely by decelerating automobile engines and refineries. Under the influence of sunlight, the combustion products, nitrogen oxides, break down the petroleum vapors into what chemists call "free radicals," or molecule fragments, which then unite in a bewildering array of new chemicals, some of them deleterious to man. Also the additives in gasoline, notably lead, a long-recognized poison, are released to the atmosphere.

Perhaps the most dangerous product resulting from exhaust gases under the influence of the famed sunshine of Los Angeles is ozone. Far from being an invigorating "superoxygen" as once thought, ozone is actually as deadly as any chemical pollutant with which we have yet had to contend. Men who have deliberately exposed themselves in gas chambers to air containing two parts of ozone per million can vouch for the potency of its poison. For the first half-hour little effect of exposure is noticed, but during the second half-hour one suffers from chest constrictions. The third half-hour finds one having difficulty concentrating, and by the fourth he is literally drunk. Several days are required for a healthy man to recover full vitality after just a two-hour exposure, and several weeks likely will elapse before a resultant cough disappears.

The present status of atmospheric contamination may be compared to the "dust era" that followed advent of the automobile early in this century. As motoring became popular a new problem arose because of no hard-surfaced roads, the problem of "abominable dust," from which it was said there "seems at present to be absolutely no escape." Though the first attempt at a solution was to keep speed limits below dust-raising levels, the eventual answer was, of course, to build extensive and costly highways. If the terrific cost and the vastness of our present road network had then been comprehended, such a solution would have been scoffed at as completely unattainable and impractical. But just as we did not then give up our cars, so we will not now relinquish them even though they are a major source of air contamination, and we cannot think of closing our factories or doing without furnaces. We must therefore be prepared to bear the considerable expense purifying our air will entail, because the air cannot be further defiled with impunity. Soon the phrase "as free as the air we breathe" will no longer have its intended connotation.

Aside from cost, the problem will not be easy to solve. Sources of contaminants, climatic conditions, and surrounding terrain all make air pollution an enigma peculiar to each area. On top of that, the experts do not always agree on what the pollutants are and to what extent they are hazardous. Most citizens know, nevertheless, when they suffer eye and throat irritations, when visibility is poor, and when there is vegetation or paint damage. As a result civic, industrial, private, and legislative groups are stirring into action. The federal government through its Public Health Service is undertaking broad surveying, instructing, and research studies. Cities like Pittsburgh, where once the sun was rarely seen, or St. Louis, where street lights in midmorning were not unusual, have rid themselves of much smoke, soot, and ash contamination. They did so largely by substituting natural gas for the soft coal they once burned. Future improvements may not be so simple. Suggestions have varied between attaching massive machines to each furnace and use of solar energy, the latter by painting alternate city blocks white and black to promote convection currents. Getting rid of automobile fumes will probably require conversion equipment for each auto as well as fuel changes. What the nature of converters will be cannot now be said, but satisfactory devices are being avidly sought. United States industries, including automobile manufacturers, and local communities are spending some $150,000,000 a year on pollution abatement and research. Such efforts are still localized, however, and amount only to a respectable beginning.

Though much thought and effort today are rightly directed toward clearing our air of contaminants, including smoke, it is not inconceivable that the day may come when smoke will prove a blessing, when dense clouds of it may intentionally be produced over cities. Smoke could prevent some damage during a nuclear attack, and although we shudder at the thought of such a black day, the fact remains that one is possible. With killing intensity, heat radiation from a nuclear or atomic explosion reaches well beyond the blast area if the air is clear, but it cannot penetrate opaque substances; heavy smoke would thus decrease burns and limit fires in outlying sections. But smoke would be no protection whatsoever from blast or radioactivity. Cities directly attacked with thermonuclear bombs would suffer a near-mortal blow, explosion and flame leaving them a jumbled, twisted wreckage of steel and mortar as complete as if they had been constructed of cardboard. The death toll would rise in moments to hundreds of thousands, even millions in an all-out attack. The target cities, moreover, would not be alone for long in their travail. Radioactive dust from each explosion would be spread for hundreds of miles by the prevailing winds. Twelve hours after a bomb explosion in San Francisco, deadly dust would be falling in Montana and Wyoming. An explosion in Detroit would send a lethal cloud to Washington, D.C. It is not idle talk to say that the shadow of absolute annihilation from radioactive poisoning hangs over the entire human race. Eniwetok is far from Johannesburg, and a great distance separates Siberia and Chicago, but an atmospheric disturbance at one place is eventually felt at all others through the circulation of the winds.

Weapons tests are the chief source of artificial air-borne radioactivity at the present time [Plate 8]. Despite elaborate precautions, even these have had serious consequences, thus revealing in a small way the global disaster that would follow if a nuclear war erupted. At 6:12 A.M., March 1, 1954, a great thermonuclear explosion was set off in the Pacific. It blasted an island into smithereens and destroyed a scientific concept as well. Previously, radioactive hazards were thought to be confined to the immediate vicinity of a nuclear explosion, but then we learned that terrific quantities of radioactive dust could be spread over thousands of square miles. Several groups of people happened to be in the path of this particular radioactive fall-out: fishermen on the Japanese trawler *Lucky Dragon*, American weather observers and natives on islands near Bikini, and Marshall Islanders.

Appearing as a second sunrise to the Japanese fishermen, the explosion was watched with awe. Some six minutes later, hence at a distance of about seventy miles from the explosion, they heard a loud rumble like thunder. In about two hours a fine, white, snow-like ash began to fall on the trawler. At first it hurt the eyes of the crew, and later their skin began to itch and then finally to burn. Before any formal treatment was begun the *Lucky Dragon* sailed to Japan. There one of the fishermen died and the other twenty-two members of the crew were hospitalized suffering from various degrees of radiation sickness. The Americans and Bikini natives were promptly evacuated and escaped relatively unscathed. The fates of sixty-four Marshallese, whose island received a moderate fall-out of radioactive debris, show most clearly what transpires after exposure.

The dust that fell some hours after the detonation caused tears to run from their eyes and their skin to itch and burn just as it had the Japanese fishermen. During the first night three-fourths of the group were nauseated. Two days later our navy discovered their plight, removed them from the island, and vigorously tried to decontaminate them. By this time the first symptoms had disappeared, but two weeks later the patients developed new ones. Patches of skin rose up in leathery welts, sometimes to peel away, revealing white or pink tissue. More severe burns wept and formed crusts. The hair of three-fourth of the individuals came out in handfuls. But these external burns, under the devoted care of squads of navy doctors, finally healed, leaving only discoloration and scars. The internal effects on the victims' blood were more long-lasting. Subsequent tests revealed that their white blood cells were greatly reduced in number for a period of six months. The Marshallese were saved only by removal from their contaminated island; the effects during their later life and on their progeny will be followed closely.

Fall-out, such as that which caught these Pacific victims, is a composite of earth, dust, water drawn up by the blast, vaporized parts of the bomb itself, and compounds produced from atmospheric gases. Borne by the wind, this debris gradually falls back to earth in a cigar-shaped pattern, with the most deadly contamination nearest the point of the explosion. Even so, a moderate-sized H-bomb could spread a concentration similar to that received by the Marshallese over 100,000 square miles, an area more than twice that of New York State. Fall-out from an air explosion, when the fireball does not reach the ground, constitutes a lesser danger because not so much debris is thrown into the air. Nevertheless, radioactivity could still be released in quantities sufficient to upset the natural conditions to which all life on earth is adapted if bombs long continued to be exploded.

First, an H-bomb forms tremendous amounts of nitric acid from atmospheric oxygen, nitrogen, and water vapor. This acid causes the burning eyes and skin and the nausea; it would adversely affect the vegetation of an area subjected to H-bomb attack. Secondly, released neutrons convert atmospheric nitrogen in great quantities to carbon 14, a radioactive isotope that decays slowly over thousands of years. Absorbed by plants, carbon 14 eventually enters the tissue of animals and humans (see Chapter 3). Finally, a hundred or so radioactive elements are produced from the atom-bomb trigger, the uranium jacket, and matter in the earth or sea if the explosion is at a low level. This radioactivity is more frightening than the awesome destructive power of the bomb itself.

Radioactivity is the peculiar trait of certain unstable elements, which decay by radiating energy in a manner somewhat analogous to the radiation of heat from a lump of coal as it decays into ashes. We can neither see, feel, hear, taste, nor smell radioactive radiations, and exposure to them may antedate by weeks or years any ascertainable biological effects; the Hiroshima and Nagasaki explosions, for example, are still claiming victims. But the results may not be spectacular or even conspicuous. Radioactivity is not something new to human beings; man has always lived in a radioactive cauldron. Our bodies contain radioactive potassium, which continually gives off X-rays; carbon atoms are forever disintegrating within us; cosmic rays and rays from radium and uranium in the earth bombard us incessantly. In the preatomic era the human species' recuperative power managed to stay ahead of this damage. Precisely how much more radioactivity we can tolerate has not been established, but it is precious little. It may well be that every bit of radiation, no matter how small, exacts its toll. Statistics show, for example, that physicians who have no contact with radiation live on the average five years longer than radiologists.

From the first hundred or so nuclear bombs exploded by the United States, Russia, and Britain, an estimated one ton of radioactive material was set adrift in the atmosphere. Though seemingly insignificant, this amount is possibly one billion times more deadly than an equal weight of one of our most poisonous industrial gases, chlorine. At this very moment the stratosphere holds at least forty pounds of radioactive strontium put there mostly by superbomb tests, and this strontium (strontium 90) is perhaps the most dangerous of all fission-born radioactive substances. Chemically like calcium, strontium is taken up by plants in the place of calcium, and finds its way into the bones of animals and humans when the plants are eaten. A detectable amount has already been accumulated by us all. Scientists of Columbia University's Lamont Geological Laboratory have been able to find traces of radioactive strontium in fresh human bones collected from hospitals in widely scattered parts of the earth, leading them to conclude that "at the present time, strontium 90 can be found in all human beings, regardless of age or geographic location." Even if there are no more H-bomb explosions, our bones will continue to accumulate strontium as it trickles down from the stratosphere. By 1970 every person's bones will contain fifteen to twenty times as much as now. Children will accumulate much more than adults in coming years because they are growing; those of the Northern Hemisphere more than Southern Hemisphere residents because the great majority of explosions to date have occurred north of the equator. We in the United States and particularly those of the eastern part of the country have received more radioactivity than peoples of other lands because prevailing winds bring particles to us from our own tests in Nevada and the Central Pacific as well as those from the Russian tests in Siberia.

If all this atmospheric strontium reached the earth's inhabitants, it would be more than enough to inflict a slow, agonizing death on us all through cancer and leukemia. The strontium and other radioactive materials in their present concentrations actually will spread slowly throughout the earth, where their effects can probably never be detected in census, longevity, or medical data. Even so, few doubt that this radioactivity will cause some bone cancer, leukemia, and similar illnesses. Geneticists believe there must inevitably be an increase in mutation, a change during the process of tender cell growth and reproduction resulting in an imperfect copy of the parent. While most mutations are mild, amounting in humans to a susceptibility to disease or a shortening of life, they can mean two heads and horribly distorted bodies and minds in coming generations. In terms of any individual's chances of being afflicted, radiation danger presently is far less than many other hazards of life; but on the other hand, an effect that concerns only a fraction of 1 per cent of the world's population can still involve tens of thousands of persons. Even if, as has been calculated, man-made radioactivity has reduced world-wide life expectancy by only two days, some lives will be reduced by years to make up for the great majority who will be unaffected.

As of the present, the consensus seems to be that several hundred times as many H-bombs can be exploded as already have been before levels of radioactivity are reached where effects would build up rapidly and indisputably. If the rate of bomb tests for the years 1955 and 1956 are not exceeded, this gives about a century. By 1954's rate, on the other hand, it means twelve to fifteen years. Clearly, even a "small war" could severely cut into this margin of safety. Just as clearly, the world's growing nuclear power program will create radiation problems. In 1956, committees of the National Academy of Sciences, projecting present indications into the future, reported it likely that by the year 2000 such plants will have produced the gas krypton 85 in quantities sufficient to have raised appreciably the radioactivity of the middle latitudes of the Northern Hemisphere. On a local scale, heavy gases like iodine 131 will have raised the radioactivity in the vicinity of the plants still more. Should a major accident occur in the year 2000 to one of the larger power plants likely then to be in existence, the committee foresees the possibility of enough strontium 90 being dispersed to contaminate the entire earth.

As if to provide a preview of the kind of accident that may haunt the atomic future, trouble developed at Britain's Windscale plutonium plant in the fall of 1957. Deep in the massive graphite structure of a reactor, a canister of uranium grew white hot from its own fierce radioactivity and began to burn in the old-fashioned chemical way. Before the fire could be extinguished, some of its "smoke" escaped, eventually settling on the surrounding countryside. The escaped radioactivity was not large, but after a few days milk from cows eating contaminated grass was found to be spiked with radioiodine. No sample of milk was found to be really dangerous, but because human beings concentrate iodine from their food in the thyroid glands, a ban was placed on milk produced in a two-hundred-square-mile area. Beef cattle in the area, similarly concentrating iodine in the thyroids, were also marked so that these glands could be destroyed immediately after the animals were slaughtered.

This ability of certain animals, plants, and parts of the human body to concentrate enormously specific radioactive elements points up a present potential hazard from the radioactivity already spread about the earth. Radioiodine and strontium, as shown, largely end in the thyroid glands and bones, respectively. Our eyes concentrate copper, our kidneys ruthenium, our liver silver, and our spleen polonium. Radioactive cobalt is collected by certain clams through such a selective biological mechanism that the concentration of this element is raised from an undetectable amount in the environment to a level where the consumption of a few would be dangerous. Sea squirts, small marine animals, are highly efficient collectors of radioactive vanadium. The tea plant is an avid seeker after ordinary manganese and presumably will also concentrate the radioactive kind. Many more such examples of tremendous concentrating power are almost certain to exist, and they must be sought out continually as radioactivity levels rise.

Although there are other great gaps in our knowledge, radio-activity is a better-understood quantity in many respects than chemical pollution. For nearly half a century before atomic fission was discovered, natural radioactivity, X-rays, and cosmic rays were studied. In view of the great strides that have been made, scientists very likely can come up with solutions to permit full utilization of atomic energy with little radiation danger if thinking and responsible statesmen can circumvent the radioactive holocaust that war might bring.

Unfortunately, even if international agreements lead ultimately to restrictions on atomic armaments, other deadly air-borne poisons such as so-called nerve gases and bacterial agents remain. Although there has never been a movement afoot for control of these poisons, enforcement of restrictions, if there were such, would be extremely difficult. These agents are difficult to detect, and they can be manufactured in meager industrial establishments, perhaps even in widely dispersed laboratories disguised as legitimate research institutions. Unlike nuclear weapons, which would destroy factories, buildings, and the entire wealth of an area, they can either kill or incapacitate a people while leaving property intact. Psychochemical agents may even be developed that are capable of upsetting behavior patterns, thereby making it possible to produce temporary irrationality in an area's population, to the great advantage of an enemy. Since man has rarely hesitated to use whatever weapons he could get his hands on if he thought they gave him an advantage, it would be the height of folly to assume that he would behave differently in the case of gases and bacteria. Military men do not treat this possibility lightly.

When the Germans released chlorine gas on April 22, 1915, they were by no means the first to use chemical gases in military operations. In the siege of Plataea, 428 B.C., the Spartans burned wood saturated with pitch and sulfur to create poisonous choking fumes. During the days of the Roman Empire, similar burning compounds were thrown into cities by the military engines ordinarily employed for hurling rocks and javelins. Other methods of destruction gained eminence in later years, but chemical gases were not forgotten. Admiral Lord Dundonald submitted a plan to the English government during the siege of Sebastopol, 1855, to vaporize huge quantities of sulfur in a favorable wind in order to suffocate the garrisons of Russian forts. The plan was admitted feasible, but was never put into effect. In our own War Between the States, one John W. Doughty of New York City suggested to the War Department in Washington that chlorine gas would be a potent weapon, but his suggestion was apparently dismissed without so much as an acknowledgement. By the time of World War I, the principal combatants were nations highly developed in science. Germany was a world leader in chemistry, and logically turned to chemicals to break the stalemate of trench warfare. The results were immediate, effective, and cheap; had Germany been prepared to press her advantage, the outcome of the war might have been quite different. The gas troops in the armies on both sides totaled only a little more than seventeen thousand, yet they inflicted more than a million and a quarter casualties before the war was over. Poisonous gases were not used in World War II simply because every nation knew that retribution in kind would follow immediately.

Although gases were cheap in World War I, they are relatively much cheaper and infinitely more dangerous today. The original war gases are still available, but far more fearsome ones have been developed, though as yet not used. From an insecticide-seeking program undertaken in Germany during the 1930's came the discovery of simple phosphorous compounds that, in addition to being excellent insect-killers, showed a high degree of toxicity to animals. Disappearing behind elaborate security regulations, these compounds emerged during World War II as tabun, soman, and sarin, the nerve gases.

Their exact toxicity for humans, if it has been determined, has not been revealed, but it is much greater than hydrogen cyanide, itself an extremely deadly poison. Nerve gases are not only toxic upon inhalation; they are also absorbed through the skin and eyes, the latter being especially sensitive. As the name implies, they affect the transmission of nerve impulses to muscles and other nerves in a fashion analogous to the switch in an electric circuit; death almost immediately follows contact with them. Many nations have large stocks of nerve gas. Russia, for example, captured several hundred tons during her invasion of Germany and is known to be very active in research with them. Very probably the existence of several stocks has been the main deterrent to their use.

Biological warfare—the spreading of living organisms and their toxic products to cause death or illness in man and damage to crops or animals—is, like gas warfare, nothing new. Though it has not been used to a great extent in modern times, it is one of the oldest weapons of war and one effectively employed on numerous occasions. Dead rats infected with plague were catapulted by ancient armies over the walls of beleaguered cities. During the Indian wars in this country, blankets of smallpox victims were left for the Indians to steal and thus contract the disease.

The arsenal from which biological agents might be selected includes, first, all the common diseases to which man, his domesticated animals, and his crops are heir. If an enemy wished to eradicate large numbers of people, he would probably have his planes scatter typhus, plague, cholera, or smallpox, being careful first to immunize his own. If only to cripple by making people sick is called for, he could attack with rabbit or undulant fever. Domestic animals could be infected with anthrax or glanders, poultry with fowl pest or Newcastle disease, cattle and sheep with rinderpest. Blights might be used against green vegetables and cereals.

Although nothing definite has been revealed, it is very possible that new disease agents lurk behind guarded doors around the world, for it is well known that germs and viruses are given to mutation when bombarded with X-rays or subjected to certain chemical alterations. Being new and different, such agents would not be checked by the natural immunity we have to many diseases, and their effects might be as dreadful and devastating as the influenza pandemic of 1918-1919, most likely started when a virus that had for centuries caused a distressing but seldom fatal disease suddenly turned virulent through mutation. It has even been suggested that an indirect result of the radiations resulting from bomb tests could be deadlier germs and viruses, hence new and spreading epidemics.

Thus the road mankind is traveling can lead to ultimate annihilation. He faces the development of an atmospheric cancer, a worldwide malignancy, unless he learns to resolve international problems peaceably. With less urgency, perhaps, but with equal fervor he must check also the wanton pollution of the atmosphere that even now is lowering our vitality and our enjoyment of life. Just as we have learned the necessity of pure food and drink, we must realize the value of clean air. We no longer allow open sewers in our cities, and we must cease to tolerate the discharge of waste effluvia into the air.

14 the vertical frontier

There is no easy road from the earth to the stars. (Non est ad astra mollis e terris via.)

SENECA

ANOTHER HORIZON is ever ahead, another goal to be striven toward. Only a little more than fifty years ago man lifted himself a few feet off the ground in his first airplane; now he navigates the air more readily than any bird and makes plans for trips to the moon. Though recent artificial satellite and rocket accomplishments on the fringes of the atmosphere have been spectacular, major hurdles are yet to be vaulted a few score miles overhead in the untamed atmospheric borderland that has been aptly termed the vertical frontier.

Venture on the threshold of space might well have been prompted by the noblest aspirations of mankind, but the prime motivating influence, at least in this country, is national security. Military technology, outgrowing the earth's surface in World War I and rising into the stratosphere during the second world conflict, now soars toward the near-vacuum above us. Competence in all the regions overhead is indeed a matter of necessity, and startling changes can be expected as a matter of course. Today's accomplishments will be as outdated as the dodo in a few years.

The airy frontier's boundary is commonly put about six hundred miles out, the highest level at which aurora phenomena are observed, but such a limit has little real significance. Critical regions are reached for human beings when the air is no longer sufficient for breathing, when it cannot cut out primordial cosmic rays, when it does not diffuse sunlight, or when it becomes a poison rather than a life-giver. The limiting boundaries for planes and balloons are reached when mechanical support cannot be attained; for high-speed planes and rockets, when a balanced exchange of heat is impossible. Already vehicles with human and animal cargoes have passed some of these boundaries and bumped into others. In these cases, conditions can grow little more rigorous no matter how much farther is reached. Truly the conquest of space has begun!

But as this is written the pinnacle of human ascent is barely two dozen miles, and this for only a moment in an experimental rocket plane. Sixteen hours above ninety thousand feet is the longest and highest that man has remained aloft, the latter being achieved by a balloon with its human cargo hermetically sealed in an aluminum, telephone-booth-size gondola. The difficulties to be surmounted are shown by the fact that literally years of planning and training preceded this mission, though from start to finish it lasted less than a day and a half. The occupant was himself both a physicist and a physician. Before the attempt he drilled endlessly through simulated emergencies, practiced living in the capsule, and learned the art of parachute jumping. Throughout the flight his heartbeat and respiration rate were radioed to a monitoring physiologist. Film was strapped to his body to record the tracks of secondary cosmic rays that plowed into him. Radar followed the balloon's drift, and meteorologists kept tabs on the weather. Inside the gondola were controls for the balloon and scores of instruments, including altimeter, temperature and pressure indicators, cameras, and the viewing end of a telescope.

While demonstrating human survival to be possible above 99 per cent of the earth's atmosphere, the flight mainly confirmed that many technological battles had yet to be won before human beings could escape from and then return to the atmospheric environment. Further, it demonstrated that the greatest obstacle to higher and faster flying is not a lack of technology but is simply human frailty. Man's body, having been molded through the ages for conditions below the treetops, has no defenses in the air-deficient heavens; he is as much out of his element there as is a salmon in the Sahara. Thus the step into the upper atmosphere and beyond is comparable, at least, to the transition from aquatic animals to amphibians in geologic times, an evolutionary process that required at least a hundred million years. Now, however, even the magic of gradual change is of little consequence. In fact, there is no chance of life ever adapting to a near-void environment. Only through the combined efforts of all sciences—biology, physics, chemistry, astronomy, and engineering—can we hope to cope with the new conditions.

As everyone knows, we require oxygen to live, but very few realize that we would die if we did not have it under rather narrow limits of pressure. Upon inhaling, the chest wall and diaphragm pull away from the lungs, but the lungs themselves are not expanded by the movement. Air under pressure must force its way inside our bodies. Thus as air pressure diminishes our lungs are less and less able to drink their fill of life-giving oxygen. Our lungs also, particularly when the pressure becomes very low, are blocked with the water vapor and carbon dioxide of which our bodies are trying to rid themselves. A man in a low-pressure region could quite literally drown in the water vapor he was trying to exhale.

Although the air thins out rapidly with altitude, human beings are inappreciably affected by the decrease in the air's pressure below an elevation of 7000 feet. Above this elevation unacclimatized persons begin to suffer from sleeplessness and a vague sort of lassitude known for years as "mountain sickness." Beyond the 10,000- to

12,000-foot level lack of sufficient oxygen leads to anemia and muscular weakness in many permanent mountain inhabitants. Newcomers experience fuzzy sight, dulled senses of hearing, taste, and smell, weakened facilities of decision and judgment, and symptoms like alcoholic intoxication in general. Above some 16,000 or 17,000 feet the average individual suffers strange delusions, loses consciousness, and may even go into convulsions. By gradual acclimatization over periods of months or years, explorers training for an assault on high mountains like the Himalayas have adapted themselves to live in conditions found as high as 25,000 feet. But an average person suddenly exposed to the rarefied air at this level, as a pilot might be if the compression system of his plane failed, will lose consciousness in three or four minutes.

At higher altitudes, the time of useful consciousness after exposure dwindles rapidly. At 30,000 feet the interval has become roughly one minute, and at 50,000 it is reduced to some fifteen seconds. Thus, as far as a supply of oxygen is concerned, space is attained at an altitude of ten miles. In order to maintain life at this level a pressurized envelope or capsule is essential. Bubbles of plastic covering only the head, as often depicted by artists for the costume of space explorers, will not suffice; for, beyond a source of air under pressure, protection for the entire body must be provided to prevent the water in body tissues from expanding into vapor and tearing the very body cells apart. An enclosed capsule means, in addition, that exhaled gases and the other products of metabolic processes must be removed if normal activity is to be assured for more than short periods of time. At about 63,000 feet, the air pressure is so low that water boils at the temperature of human blood. If exposed even for an instant here, the blood would turn into a bubbly froth and death would follow.

Enclosed in a protective pressurized cabin and physically protected, a man faces other difficulty at high altitudes. With the earth and clouds far below, there are only the objects about him on which to focus his eyes. His depth of perception becomes hazy, and his alertness diminishes. A strange psychological phenomenon, given the name break-off, is experienced by jet pilots who fly alone at high altitudes. They begin to feel that all connections with the earth have been severed and that they are in another world. For some the experience is exhilarating; others become anxious or nervous and even fear to move. The effect, fortunately, disappears when attention is forced back to problems of the flight, but that such a condition can exist is obviously fraught with danger.

The quality of sunlight also is vastly changed with altitude. There being fewer air molecules and dust particles to diffuse it, sunlight is much more powerful than at the earth's surface, and shadows cast are completely black. A pilot cannot see his instruments in the shadows unless they are lighted. Human eyes, not being designed to adjust rapidly from complete darkness to full sunlight, suffer from light shock. To glance at the sun for an instant would be disastrous. Even to look upon a sunlit object nearby after having gazed at the general blackness of the sky will dazzle the eyes dangerously. In the shadow of the earth everything is, of course, as dark as the star-strewn heavens on a moonless night.

At about 70,000 feet an altitude is reached where combustion becomes impossible. Terrestrial power plants such as the familiar reciprocating and jet engines are useless. At present only rockets that carry their own oxygen can operate beyond this point. At 80,000 feet such air as remains becomes poisonous because of ozone, the superactive cousin of oxygen. Pressurizing the outside air with mechanical compressors is useless from here on up; a sealed cabin with a built-in air supply is necessary to sustain life.

A little higher, at 90,000 to 120,000 feet, the protective ceiling against ultraviolet and cosmic radiations is pierced. Here ultraviolet radiation, the sunburning factor, is about ten times as great as it is under a noonday sun at sea level. Fortunately, thin walls of a great many materials will ward off these rays, so they do not present as serious a problem as some others. The same is not true for cosmic rays; they can penetrate many feet of steel plate.

Primary cosmic rays are atomic particles, some of which are as heavy as atoms of iron. They travel at terrific velocities and come mostly from the depths of space, though from precisely where no one knows. Upon reaching the fringes of the atmosphere they normally collide with air molecules and smash themselves into a shower of lesser fragments, which then pepper the earth. Since life began, it has had to contend with this relatively gentle shower of cosmic rays, but it has not experienced the piercing bombardment of the primary rays. Very little is known at present about their effects on sensitive body cells. It is certain, however, that cells receiving direct hits succumb to the tiny bullets, and many dead cells in a tissue cause that tissue to become unhealthy.

Recent balloon and rocket tests with mice, monkeys, dogs, guinea pigs, rats, chicken eggs, human tissue, fungi, and men have been re-assuring in regard to exposure to the primary rays. Enclosed in air-conditioned and pressurized capsules, two monkeys have logged sixty-three hours suspended from balloons above 90,000 feet. While there they ate, moved about, saw, and heard just as on the ground. Though for a considerable time in the region where cosmic rays were rampant, they have yet shown no adverse effects. Some black mice grew a few white hairs after similar experiences, presumably as a result of cosmic rays passing through hair follicles, but no real damage was detected here either. From this it is assumed that not enough cells will be destroyed, upon short exposure at least, to affect seriously normal bodily functions. Genetic damage is a differ-ent matter. When a cosmic ray hits a reproductive cell the birth of an imperfect individual may result. The unpleasant possibility can-not be ruled out at the present that, should humans remain for some time above much of the atmosphere, damaged genes in reproductive cells would result in a high rate of mutation, perhaps even in still-born or deformed children. Bread molds, at least, exposed to the upper-atmospheric atomic storm have shown mutations.

At 300,000 feet, or roughly sixty miles, atmospheric protection from meteorities is passed. Again, the exact magnitude of the danger is unknown, but a rather large number of foreign bodies, mostly tiny micrometeorites, plunge into the atmosphere each day, at velocities initially as great as forty miles a second. By virtue of their terrific speed they have penetrating powers up to ten thousand times, pound for pound, that of a rifle bullet, but their small size will permit most to be stopped by the walls of any chamber otherwise sufficient to protect a man. Confirming evidence of both contentions is supplied by rockets that leave the earth with smooth, shiny surfaces and return with their skins pitted and scarred from innumerable collisions after vertical trips of a few hundred miles. Our satellite micrometeorite detectors have also registered encounters. Though the chances of an encounter between a man-carrying vehicle and a rather large meteorite, say of marble size, seem about as remote as a rendezvous between two blind bees having sole occupancy of a cubic mile of space, when a large meteorite is met it will crash through a protective chamber as a rifle bullet might pierce a tin can. The consensus, nevertheless, is that meteoric hazards are minor in comparison to other recognized ones.

Like its pilot, any aircraft or rocket ship has limitations that change drastically with altitude. The degree to which the atmosphere gives mechanical support depends on the speed of flight as well as the height of operation. At an elevation of 120 miles interaction between air and aircraft is essentially nonexistent regardless of speed and wing shape. This level might thus be considered the mechanical beginning of space, and if a craft could operate without approaching closer than this to the earth, its shape would be a matter of little consequence. As it is the sleek, graceful, needlelike outline of present planes and rockets is dictated by the properties of air, for any object moving through the air is always sheathed with an invisible film that must be dragged along. This adhering film of air is called a boundary layer, and making it behave presents formidable problems in aerodynamics, particularly at high speeds.

An adhering fluid film is peculiar to neither air nor aircraft. A submarine cruising beneath the sea drags a layer of water with it. As ordinary a thing as a pitcher from which syrup has been poured on pancakes shows that a film of fluids clings to its wall. The air-boundary layer is not nearly as sticky as syrup, or even as water, but nevertheless within it resides most of the resistance to aircraft movement. When the layer can be kept thin and moving, without waves or ripples, the drag on an aircraft is greatly reduced; but if the boundary layer breaks over into turbulence, as it is wont to do at high speeds, the resistance offered by the air is increased many times. By way of illustration, smooth flow and turbulent flow both may be distinguished in the smoke rising from a cigarette through still air. Drifting upward immediately above the burning zone is a smooth-flowing filament of smoke. After traveling a few inches the filament begins to oscillate, and then a short distance farther its movement becomes erratic, or turbulent. When this happens with a high-speed plane, serious troubles develop. To eliminate boundary-layer turbulence, such unlikely things as wings of porous or perforated material are being tested. With these the stagnant layer next to the plane is partly withdrawn in through the plane to prevent it from growing thick and possibly turbulent. Under other circumstances cooling liquid is pumped through the perforated skin to make the plane, in effect, perspire, the latter development helping in the solution of another problem peculiar to aircraft traveling at and beyond supersonic speeds.

The picture of a pilot bundled in a heavy suit was familiar to everyone a few years ago, for it was quite obvious that extra protection was required in the icy altitudes. Strangely, the problem is now reversed, high temperatures setting very definite limitations. A fast-flying airplane or missile acts like a piston, compressing and heating the air before its nose and leading wing edges. Back along the plane, friction further heats the boundary-layer air, so that at the speeds attained today the craft can literally be bathed in a film of flame. A rocket is enveloped in air heated to more than 2000 degrees Fahrenheit when pushed along through the air at a speed of about 3500 miles per hour. Airplanes flying at 2000 miles an hour can encounter heat intense enough to melt rubber and plastic, to cause lubricants and fuel to boil away, to make aluminum grow weak like butter, and to roast a man. Even at 1000 miles per hour the skin of an airplane attains a temperature of 180 degrees, far higher than a pilot can stand for long without elaborate refrigeration equipment. In the laboratory relative movement of 18,000 miles an hour between an object and air has been found to create a temperature of 15,000 degrees, far hotter than the surface of the sun. The temperature is, furthermore, the same regardless of air pressure. But because of less air at high altitudes, the quantity of heat there is greatly diminished. Consequently, highest speeds can be attained only at great heights.

The quantity of heat that can be involved due to the compression effect is truly fantastic. A fighter plane flying at 1500 miles an hour may create as much as 170,000,000 British thermal units of heat in five minutes, or about as much as 45,000 home furnaces produce in the same time. Moreover, within the atmosphere there can never be a complete breakthrough of the thermal barrier, as air-friction heating has come to be called. In fact, airplane flight is faced with something of a dilemma. Climbing higher and higher reduces the amount of heat produced, but the limit of mechanical support is soon reached. Very likely each additional increment of airplane speed for some time to come will be won by extra refrigeration for the pilot and better heat-resisting materials for his plane.

For short periods a man can endure rather high temperatures, but in those conditions that planes are now encountering, this reserve of time for useful activity is a matter of minutes. Though it varies with the amount and type of clothing, something less than thirty minutes would be available to a man in which to save himself if his cooling system failed and his craft's cabin temperature suddenly rose to that of boiling water. At 300 degrees Fahrenheit the time drops to only a dozen minutes, and at 500 degrees exposure can be tolerated for no more than three minutes without endangering health and life.

Even high-altitude rockets, missiles, and spaceships cannot escape the thermal barrier, for, presumably, each will have to return to earth sometime. Returning may, in fact, be a much more difficult problem than escaping, for a rocket accelerates relatively slowly and, on the outward leg of the trip, will not have to attain highest speeds until well above most of the atmosphere. Thus it can avoid excessive frictional heating on the outgoing trip. But upon its attempting the return, the earth and its atmosphere will be approached at high speeds. Theoretically, at least, a rocket might slow down gradually by skimming through the outer fringes of the air in a circling orbit, moving slowly closer to the earth while always keeping at a distance where the air's density and the rocket's speed are insufficient to melt its structure. In practice, such a precision maneuver would be difficult indeed. As we have seen (Chapter 1), there are tides in the atmosphere just as in the ocean, and the atmosphere bulges its limits outward in anything but a uniform manner.

Perhaps before the safe-returning feat is attempted we will have much tougher and better insulating materials. So far most high-altitude rockets and earth satellites have come to violent ends, the rockets smashing everything not protected in strong steel boxes and the satellites being consumed as a result of their frictional heat. In some cases experimental rockets have been deliberately blown apart during descent to destroy their streamlining and make the pieces fall more slowly, thereby preserving some instrument records that otherwise would have been lost. In other tests, rockets have been deliberately blasted back toward the earth to pierce the air so rapidly that the heat generated has insufficient time to penetrate into the instruments contained inside. But such a maneuver hardly seems practical with a living passenger aboard. Parachutes also have been used, but they have not proved completely effective for returning rockets. Though made of steel ribbons or strands, the chutes on occasion have melted during the descent.

In the outer regions of the earth's atmosphere—that is, beyond 120 miles—temperature will still be a problem, albeit an entirely different one. Any man-carrying vehicle there will have its temperature determined solely by the interchange of radiation between it, the sun, and the earth, for the air's molecules are too few and too far apart to cause either heat or cold. Though still ninety-two million miles away, the sun's radiation is sufficiently strong to raise to intolerable levels the temperature of an object absorbing the sun's energy and not reradiating it away rapidly. Ordinary materials of construction differ widely in their behavior before radiant energy. Polished aluminum, for example, absorbs well and radiates poorly. A vehicle having a skin of aluminum would be expected to reach 700 or 800 degrees Fahrenheit. By contrast, a coating of white-pigmented paint would make the vehicle reflect so well that its temperature would stabilize at some 60 degrees below zero. Of course, it should be possible to select a material or combination of materials that would maintain a comfortable balance. But the balance could be easily upset. In the shadow of the earth temperatures would drop precipitously; or if for any reason the white coating should peel off and expose polished aluminum, the ship would become a crematory for the persons inside.

As will be recalled from Chapter 3, other radiations, notably the protons and electrons that produce the auroras, rain in unchecked fury upon the upper atmosphere. Beginning at an altitude of about six hundred miles and extending outward for unknown thousands more, these atomic particles, probably concentrated in a belt-like pattern thickest above the equator by the earth's magnetic field, are thought to give rise to yet a different zone of radiation that only recently has been discovered. According to our best theories at present, when the protons or electrons collide with the substance of a satellite, or any future man-carrying vehicle, they cause a profusion of X-rays, possibly one thousand times as intense as cosmic rays, to be created. Just what limitations this will impose upon survival in the particle belt cannot now be answered, but it looks as if serious trouble were ahead for space travelers. Residence in this outer fringe of the atmosphere may well be restricted to the time necessary for direct passage through it in a high-speed rocket, unless heavy shielding is provided.

Not to be overlooked among such enumerated dangers as oxygen sparsity, heat or cold, and radiations are the invisible inertial forces associated with high velocity and directional change. Ever since the Wright brothers—who flew, incidentally, in a prone position—took to the air, accelerative forces have hampered pilots. We feel acceleration as passengers in an automobile when it is stopped or started rapidly. We feel it pulling us outward when the car rounds a sharp curve. Magnified many times, these same forces pull a pilot's blood and his internal organs to the outside of a turn, drain the blood from his head, and push abdominal organs down into the pelvic region when he is pulling out of a dive. At highest speeds, some two thousand miles an hour for a man currently, even gentle turns set up forces sufficient to distort the vision and to make an unprotected pilot black out or lose consciousness. Exposure to greater forces produces general reactions similar to those suffered during a brain concussion. Though large inertial forces can be extremely harmful, the complete absence of gravity when drifting in space or circling the earth in the outer reaches of the atmosphere may be even more serious. Difficulties with blood circulation, respiration, and dislocation of body organs will, of course, occur, but they are not likely to have permanent consequences. Disturbances with regard to orientation, to execution of body movements, and to coordination of motion are to be expected, and these could lead to emotional upsets and neuroses. Of forty-six men exposed briefly to a gravity of zero, twenty-six felt nausea and vertigo, but trained jet pilots generally have no such difficulties. This means that short term weightlessness should not prove to be a problem, and a long sojourn may have no ill effects, for Soviet monitors of the pulse of Laika, the dog in Sputnik II, reported none. The latter did show, however, that the dog's heartbeat rate increased threefold during the acceleration period required to get in orbit and then returned to normal once the orbit was established. To avoid possible effects and to make one feel more nearly normal the solution may still be to create an artificial gravity by traversing a slightly curved or zigzag course or even by rotating the vehicle.

In the search to learn how man will fare under severe acceleration or prolonged gravity disturbances, chickens have been used to good advantage. Living up to six months in a rotating device called a centrifuge which subjected them to two and one-half times the normal force of gravity, these chickens ate, drank, and carried on in their whirling home like chickens anywhere else except that young birds grew 40 to 50 per cent slower and required more than one month longer to reach maturity. The eggs produced had a decided tendency to be flat. On occasions when young chickens were removed from the centrifuge some of them responded to their new state by turning somersaults and walking backwards. Both traits, however, disappeared when the birds were returned to their orbiting.

Of more immediate concern is the very practical problem of bail-out when a failure occurs, for perfectly operating devices have yet to be built. A jet pilot streaking across the sky at the speed of sound has little chance of climbing out into the hurricane of air rushing by, and if he did the tail assembly very likely would cut him in half. The present solution is to propel the pilot, still in his seat, outward from the plane with a charge of gunpowder; for a man, it was found, can take a tremendous kick when it lasts only an instant. But this only partially solves the difficulties, because an otherwise unprotected man cannot count on surviving the effects of being hit by the wind even at present plane speeds.

The first man to survive a supersonic bail-out was a North American Aviation, Inc., test pilot, who did so in February, 1955, only by great good luck, scores of medical specialists, and six months in the hospital. Although the man was unconscious from the time of ejection from his faltering plane, the pilot's parachute opened automatically on schedule, and he was picked up in seconds after falling into the sea a short distance off shore. The blast of air that hit him the moment he left his plane ripped off his helmet, shoes, socks, gloves, even his wrist watch and ring. His arms and legs must have flailed like propeller blades, for later his shoulders and thighs were black from bruises. The skin of his nose was torn by the terrible force of the wind; his face was black from the pounding it received; a hemorrhaging eye bled almost continuously. Heart, kidneys, liver, and stomach were damaged by the terrific pressure accompanying the jarring impact of the air. Frightfully injured though he was, the pilot's eventual recovery has prompted renewed efforts in bail-out protection.

What passes for operational protective equipment today is both restrictive and cumbersome. While it attempts to equip a man so that he has some chance of coping with virtually every hazard he is likely to encounter, it greatly handicaps his flying ability. In effect, he must wear five suits, each designed for a specific job. First over the underclothes comes a two-layer suit of rubberized nylon provided with hoses to be plugged into a plane's air-conditioning system when frictional heating becomes too severe. Next is a so-called G-suit looking like a pair of rubber overalls with five built-in rubber bladders. One bladder is over the stomach, a pair encases the thighs, and two cover the lower legs. Inflated automatically by auxiliary equipment during a turning or diving maneuver, the bladders become a kind of tourniquet to check the flow of blood to the lower extremities, thus permitting a man to withstand roughly twice the inertial forces he could otherwise. Next comes a pressure suit which is inflated to maintain normal air pressure, plus gloves and helmet. For protection against cold an insulating liner is next worn, and over all a waterproof suit is added. On top of these must be draped a parachute pack, a life preserver, a cylinder of compressed oxygen, and an assortment of other hardware. Presently much research is directed toward short-time survival in the outer limits of the atmosphere and best efforts have resulted in heavy metalized suits having no joints for the arms or legs, hence very limited flexibility.

Thus equipped, bail-out from high altitudes is still no job for an amateur. Since the safest procedure is to remain in the freezing, pressureless regions no longer than necessary, parachutes should not be opened until most of the fall is accomplished. This point is critical, moreover, for if the parachute is opened before denser air has slowed the fall somewhat, the jerk could snap a neck or break a back. Also the fall must not develop into a tumbling motion, lest when denser air is reached an uncontrollable propellerlike spin results, which can rupture blood vessels in a man's eyes or head, producing unconsciousness in a matter of minutes.

Although it might appear that the upper atmosphere is completely hostile, a sober appraisal shows it to be merely neutral. Further exploration will open to us undreamed-of vistas for greater accomplishment. Undoubtedly evil can be made from the results, as it can from almost every endeavor, but hope for better things is more than justified. At any rate, the lid to a new Pandora's box has been lifted and there is no turning back.

Atomic oxygen found at an elevation of about sixty miles affords an example of things to come. Produced by the action of sunlight on regular oxygen, the atomic or stripped-down variety stores an unknown amount of energy. Though slowly disappearing at night through natural processes, atomic oxygen is renewed each day; thus its quantity should be nearly inexhaustible. Its utilization was first tested over Holloman Air Force Base, New Mexico, during the night of March 14, 1956. Carrying eighteen pounds of a rather common chemical, nitric oxide, a rocket roared into a cloudless, star-filled sky. Brilliant exhaust flames outlined its initial path, but as fuel dwindled the rocket disappeared among the stars. When the sixty-mile point was reached, preset mechanisms released the nitric oxide, and viewers below were treated to a celestial show rarely equaled.

At first a burst of light like a new star appeared in the sky. Growing swiftly, the light spot spread in ten minutes to appear four times the full moon's size and to shed something like half its light. At this stage the luminous area was three miles across. Slowly it continued to spread, dimming in the process, until finally it was visible only as a hazy streak suggestive of the Milky Way. In essence, what happened was that the nitric oxide encouraged the atomic oxygen to revert to its original form and release rapidly the energy it had imprisoned from the sun. The nitric oxide was not in the least consumed in the interchange; its effectiveness was only diminished when it spread and became diluted.

Daytime rocket experiments with nitric oxide revealed another exciting phenomenon. Under the action of the sunlight, the nitric oxide formed a cloud of electrified particles capable of reflecting radio waves almost as effectively as a mirror reflects light. A few such clouds, properly located just around the curve of the earth, might permit new and more reliable means of long-range radio communication; at night a few luminous clouds might even banish darkness if such became desirable. Perhaps the most eagerly sought use of the new discovery is propulsion, for a vehicle that can find its fuel sixty miles above the earth has obvious advantages in both peace and war. Further research may well reveal that nitric oxide is not the best means through which to produce the reaction. In fact, a solid compound has already passed its preliminary tests, opening the way to speculation that a craft may be built someday to gulp atomic oxygen through a honeycomb structure, combine the atomic variety into regular oxygen, and use the heat released to power its flight. Indeed, the region from 60 to 140 miles holds promise of being one in which the chemical energy of disassociated molecules may be tapped for propulsion.

Atomic oxygen is possibly not the only energy source to be found in the nebulous atmosphere high overhead. A metastable form of ordinary inactive nitrogen known to exist there releases energy in amounts which are large compared to our usual fuels upon reverting to its more normal state. How to make use of this energy has not been solved, but presumably the possibility is not being overlooked. Also ozone, the superactive relative of oxygen, may someday be tapped for the propulsion of globe-girdling aircraft. Sodium, likewise, when its source and occurrence are more fully understood, may open a new realm to exploitation. The latter's behavior, like that of atomic oxygen, has been probed. In this case sodium vapor carried some twenty minutes after sunset by rocket into the sunlit zone above the shadow of the earth absorbed the sun's energy and reradiated it as a brilliant orange-colored light that was visible against the dark blue sky for three hundred miles [Plate 8].*

Nuclear devices have been exploded many miles, perhaps as many

---

* The four photographs in Plate 8, taken thirty seconds apart, show the ascent and beginning of the descent of an Aerobee rocket from which was released sodium vapor. Release began at about fifty miles and continued beyond the apex at 125 miles. The lowest portions of the trail of sodium are barely visible, being in the earth's shadow. The trail balloons out at the higher elevations because of reduced atmospheric pressure, and twists and turns because of varying wind velocities at different altitudes.

as 100 miles, above the earth. One brilliant, soundless flash, visible to residents of Honolulu, occurred over Johnston Island some 700 miles southwest of Hawaii. Its purpose was to determine the behavior of an explosion in a virtual vacuum. On earth the air's pressure confines the fireball, it absorbs gamma and ultraviolet rays, and holds the radioactive debris to a comparatively small cloud. With little air at high altitudes to stop them, these radiations will expand almost indefinitely, some of the radioactive residue undoubtedly even leaving our solar system. By the time the remaining radioactive particles settle, diffusion will have spread them all about the earth and their radioactivity will have decayed nearly to insignificance.

Other promising research concerns ultraviolet radiation from the sun as well as from distant stars. Most of what we know presently about our universe comes from visible light and radio-wave measurements, atmospheric gases cutting out the other radiations. Once we are able to study the intensity and fluctuations of all stellar radiations from positions well above practically all the atmosphere, it may be possible to resolve more completely the mechanisms by which the stars fuel their atomic furnaces and to relate the results to the chemical composition of our atmosphere, to weather changes, and even to our own behavior. In fact, there is no limit to upper-air research. Chemists are eagerly awaiting an opportunity to delve into numerous photochemical reactions under the full radiation of the sun, which almost certainly will bring us new material wealth. Medicine, being forced to contend with the harsh realities of survival under extremely rigorous conditions, will of necessity advance.

From a vantage point high in the sky, the earth itself can be scrutinized as never before. Reradiations from clouds, oceans, and land will reveal how energy is stored by the earth. The earth's magnetic field can be mapped. The aurora can be studied at close range. Weather forecasters can have access to world-wide information on rainfall, storm development, and temperature such as they have never had before, with consequences that should be of inestimable value just as a storm warning alone. The International Iceberg

Patrol will no longer be needed. Even the earth's exact shape and the distances between continents can be determined with heretofore unequaled precision, making navigation safer and long-range, nuclear-armed missile aim more deadly.

This last result and all that it implies cannot, of course, be dismissed. It is possible, however, that scientific accomplishments, as suggested in these latter chapters particularly, will lead ultimately to an end of massive total wars and into a period of greater cooperation among the peoples of the world. First and most important, any other course is suicidal, for the airy realm that nurtures us all could soon be irrevocably poisoned. Two scorpions trapped in a bottle may claw and bite, but they forego administering a fatal sting, each knowing the other can retaliate in kind; human beings, this writer believes, are no less endowed with the survival instinct. Secondly, advancements in weather prediction and control, potentially of benefit to everyone, can be achieved only through international cooperation. Finally, the conquest of space should unite humanity in a common goal, one that can absorb our best efforts for generations.

If these contentions be true, then the present preoccupation with weapons of war will have borne noble fruit and, in closer harmony with our natural environment, we can look forward hopefully to a richer, fuller life.

selected reading list

The following books, scientific reports, and magazine and journal articles are presented as valuable and interesting reading material for those wishing to pursue further the subject of atmospheric phenomena.

Edward Adolphe, "Tornado Coming!" *Reader's Digest*, 68 (May 1956), 145.

John W. Anderson, "Production of Ultrasonic Sounds by Laboratory Rats and Other Mammals," *Science*, 119 (June 4, 1954), 808.

Anonymous, "Are Winters Getting Warmer?" *U. S. News and World Report*, 36 (January 8, 1954), 37.

———, "Clouds Sprayed with Dry Ice Made to Yield Rain," *Popular Mechanics*, 54 (September 1930), 418.

———, "Garbage in the Sky," *Fortune*, 51 (April 1955), 142.

———, "The Invisible Force," *General Electric Review*, 58 (May 1955), 8.

———, "Magical Waves of Silent Sound," *Compressed Air Magazine*, 55 (July, August, September 1950), 172.

———, "Probing the Upper Atmosphere," *Analytical Chemistry*, 30 (September 1958), 19A.

———, "Proceedings of the Conference on Atmospheric Electricity," *U. S. Air Force Cambridge Research Center, Geophysical Research Papers*, 42, 1955.

———, *Proceedings of the Third National Air Pollution Symposium*, Los Angeles, National Air Pollution Symposium, 1955.

———, "Project Cirrus—The Story of Cloud Seeding," *General Electric Review*, 55 (November 1952), 8.

———, *The Smog Problem in Los Angeles County*, Stanford Research Institute, January 1954.

———, "Sound Blasting the Clouds for Man-Made Weather," *Scientific American*, 128 (April 1923), 224.

———, "Tomorrow's Weather," *Fortune*, 47 (May 1953), 144.

———, "Weather or Not," *Time*, 56 (August 28, 1950), 52.

———, "What's Happening to the Weather?" *Changing Times*, 12 (August 1958), 21.

Adam Anthony, "Changes in Adrenals and Other Organs Following Exposure of Hairless Mice to Intense Sounds," *Journal of the Acoustical Society of America*, 28 (March 1954), 270.

Hidetoshi Arakawa, "Twelve Centuries of Blooming Dates of the Cherry Blossoms at the City of Kyoto and Its Own Vicinity," *Geofisica Pura e Applicata*, *30* (1955), 147.

George A. Baitsell (ed.), *Science in Progress*, New Haven, Yale University, 1953.

Werner A. Baum, "The Why of Climate," *Research Reviews* (July 1953), 7.

J. F. Bedinger, E. R. Manring, & S. N. Ghosh, "Study of Sodium Vapor Ejected into the Upper Atmosphere," *Journal of Geophysical Research*, *63* (March 1958), 19.

Francis Bello, "Hurricanes," *Fortune*, *54* (August 1956), 115.

———, "Climate: The Heat May Be Off," *Fortune*, *50* (August 1954), 108.

———, "Forecast for Weather Control: Brighter," *Fortune*, *57* (May 1958), 144.

Erik Bergaust & William Beller, *Satellite!*, Garden City, N. Y., Hanover House, 1956.

F. W. Bieberdorf & others, "Vegetation as a Measure Indicator of Air Pollution Part I. The Pine (*Pinus taeda*)," *Bulletin of the Torrey Botanical Club 85* (May-June 1958), 197.

Samuel C. Blacktin, *Dust*, London, Chapman & Hall, 1934.

Bruce Bliven, *Preview for Tomorrow: The Unfinished Business of Science*, New York, Knopf, 1953.

John W. Bond, Jr., "Problems of Aerophysics in the Hypersonic Region," *Aero Digest*, *72* (June 1956), 21.

Cicely Mary Botley, *The Air and Its Mysteries*, New York, Appleton, 1940.

E. G. Bowen, "The Relation Between Rainfall and Meteor Showers," *Journal of Meteorology*, *13* (April 1956), 142.

Roscoe R. Braham, Jr., "Life of a Thunderstorm," *Scientific American*, *182* (June 1950), 48.

C. E. P. Brooks, *Climate in Everyday Life*, London, Benn, 1950.

Harrison Brown, "The Origin of the Planets," *Chemical and Engineering News*, *30* (April 21, 1952), 1622.

Eric Burgess, *Frontier to Space*, London, Chapman & Hall, 1955.

Horace R. Byers (ed.), *Thunderstorm Electricity*, Chicago, University of Chicago, 1953.

California Dep't of Public Health, Air Pollution Study Project, *Clean Air for California*, Sacramento, 1955.

G. S. Callendar, "Can Carbon Dioxide Influence Climate?" *Weather*, *4* (October 1949), 310.

P. A. Campbell, "Atmospheric Characteristics of Great Human Significance in Aviation of the Next Decade," *Aeronautical Engineering Review, 12* (April 1953), 50.

Norman Carlisle, "Our Weather *Is* Changing," *Coronet* (Jan. 1954), 17.

J. Alan Chalmers, *Atmospheric Electricity*, New York, Pergamon, 1957.

———, "The Electrical Charge on the Earth," *Journal of Atmospheric and Terrestrial Physics, 8* (1956), 124.

Sidney Chapman, "Tides in the Atmosphere," *Scientific American, 190* (May 1954), 36.

I. Bernard Cohen, "Prejudice Against the Introduction of Lightning Rods," *Journal of the Franklin Institute, 253* (May 1952), 393.

LaMont C. Cole, "The Ecosphere," *Scientific American, 198* (April 1958), 83.

Joseph J. Cornish, III, "The Boundary Layer," *Scientific American, 191* (August 1954), 72.

Everett F. Cox, "Atomic Bomb Blast Waves," *Scientific American, 188* (April 1953), 94.

W. J. Cunningham, "Noise," *American Scientist, 43* (July 1955), 490.

J. M. DallaValle, *Micromeritics: The Technology of Fine Particles*, New York, Pitman, 1948.

Paul E. Damon and J. Laurence Kulp, "Inert Gases and the Evolution of the Atmosphere," *Geochimica et Cosmochimica Acta*, 13, No. 4 (1958), 280.

Farrington Daniels & John A. Duffie (eds.), *Solar Energy Research*, Madison, University of Wisconsin, 1955.

Bill Davidson, "Donora, The Case of the Poisoned Air," *Collier's, 124* (October 22, 1949), 30.

———, "Our Poisoned Air," *Collier's, 122* (October 23, 1948), 68.

Saville R. Davis, "What Makes It Rain?," *Reader's Digest, 64* (May 1954), 141.

Earl Devendorf & Alexander Rihm, Jr., *Proceedings of the Eleventh Industrial Waste Conference*, Lafayette, Ind., Purdue University, 1956.

Nelson Dingle, "Pollen Counts and the Hay Fever Problem," *Science, 117* (January 16, 1953), 64.

Marjory Stoneham Douglas, *Hurricane*, New York, Rinehart, 1958.

Neville Duke & Edward Lanchbery, *Sound Barrier: The Story of High-Speed Flight*, 7th ed., London, Cassell, 1954.

L. C. Dunn, "Radiation and Genetics," *Scientific Monthly, 84* (January 1957), 6.

The Editorial Staff of *Life* & Lincoln Barnett, *The World We Live In*, New York, Time, Inc., 1955.

Merril Eisenbud, "Global Distribution of Strontium-90 from Nuclear Detonations," *Scientific Monthly, 84* (May 1957), 237.

C. T. Elvey & Franklin E. Roach, "Aurora and Airglow," *Scientific American, 193* (September 1958), 140.

G. J. Fergusson, "Reduction of Atmospheric Radiocarbon Concentration by Fossil-Fuel Carbon Dioxide and the Mean Life of Carbon Dioxide in the Atmosphere," *Proceedings of the Royal Society of London, A243* (February 11, 1958), 561.

H. H. Finnell, "The Dust Storms of 1954," *Scientific American, 191* (July 1954), 25.

J. Firket, "Fog Along the Meuse Valley," *Transactions of the Faraday Society, 32* (August 1936), 1192.

Melvin W. First & Philip Drinker, "Concentrations of Particulates Found in Air," *Archives of Industrial Hygiene and Occupational Medicine, 5* (April, 1952), 387.

R. Firth, "The Weather and Atmospheric Pollution," *Institution of Public Health Engineers Journal, 57* (July 1958), 139.

Allan C. Fisher, Jr., "Aviation Medicine on the Threshold of Space," *National Geographic, 108* (August 1955), 241.

Corey Ford, "The Truth About the 'Sonic Boom'," *Saturday Evening Post, 227* (December 4, 1954), 26.

Hal Foster, "Radar and the Weather," *Scientific American, 189* (July 1953), 34.

Betty Friedan, "The Coming Ice Age," *Harper's Magazine, 217* (September 1958), 39.

Sigmund Fritz, "The Polar Whiteout," *Weather, 12* (Nov. 1957), 345.

Dan Gallery, "Pitcher In a Jam? Call the Weatherman!" *Reader's Digest, 71* (July 1957), 180.

George Gamow, *The Birth and Death of the Sun*, New York, New American Library, 1952.

T. N. Gautier, "The Ionosphere," *Scientific American, 193* (September 1955), 126.

Wilma George, "Some Animal Reactions to Variations of Temperature," *Endeavour, 12* (April 1953), 101.

George W. Gray, "Life at High Altitudes," *Scientific American, 193* (December 1955), 59.

Donald R. Griffin, "The Navigation of Bats," *Scientific American, 183* (August 1950), 52.

George W. Groh, "Quiet Please!" *American Mercury, 81* (July 1955), 11.

G. V. Groves, "Velocity of a Body Falling Through the Atmosphere and the Propagation of Its Shock Wave to Earth," *Journal of Atmospheric and Terrestrial Physics, 10* (1957), 73.

Ross Gunn, "Droplet-Electrification Processes and Coagulation in Stable and Unstable Clouds," *Journal of Meteorology, 12* (Dec. 1955), 511.

———— & B. B. Phillips, "An Experimental Investigation of the Effect of Air Pollution on the Initiation of Rain," *Journal of Meteorology, 14* (June 1957), 272.

Heinz Haber, "Flight at the Borders of Space," *Scientific American, 186* (February 1952), 20.

A. J. Hagen-Smit, "Air Conservation," *Science, 128,* 869-78 (October 13, 1958).

Roy S. Hall, "Inside a Texas Tornado," *Weatherwise, 3* (June 1951), 54.

Mark W. Harrington, "Weather Making, Ancient and Modern," *Annual Report of the Smithsonian Institution for the Year Ending June 30, 1894,* 249.

J. M. Heines, "Jet Stream Navigation," *Shell Aviation News* (February 1956), 14.

F. Hepburn, "Man's Study of Lightning," *Science Progress, 44* (1956) 635.

Mark D. Hollis, "Fresh Air Getting Scarce in U. S.?" *U. S. News and World Report, 45* (October 17, 1958), 70.

H. G. Houghton (ed.) *Atmospheric Explorations,* Cambridge and New York, Published jointly by the Technology Press and John Wiley and Sons, Inc., 1958.

Fred Hoyle, *Frontiers of Astronomy,* New York, New American Library, 1957.

————, *The Nature of the Universe,* New York, Harper, 1950.

Uno Ingärd, "A Review of the Influence of Meteorological Conditions on Sound Propagation," *The Journal of the Acoustical Society of America, 25* (May 1953), 405.

C. T. Ingold, "Spore Liberation in Higher Fungi," *Endeavour, 16* (April 1957), 78.

John Clark Johnson, *Physical Meteorology,* Cambridge, Mass., Technology Press, and New York, Wiley, 1954.

Arthur Taber Jones, *Sound,* New York, Van Nostrand, 1937.

H. Spencer Jones, *Life on Other Worlds,* New York, New American Library, 1952.

Fritz Kahn, *Design of the Universe: The Heavens and the Earth,* New York, Crown, 1954.

Martin D. Kamen, "Discoveries in Nitrogen Fixation," *Scientific American, 188* (March 1953), 38.

Joseph Kaplan and Charles A. Barth, "Chemical Aeronomy," *Proceedings of the National Academy of Sciences of the United States of America, 44* (February 1958), 105.

M. L. Kastens, "Weather to Order," *Chemical and Engineering News, 29* (March 19, 1951), 1090.

George H. T. Kimble, "The Changing Climate," *Scientific American, 182* (April 1950), 48.

Thomas A. Kindre, Jr., "Like a Bat out of . . . ," *Steelways* (December 1956), 4.

Philip J. Klass, "Meteor Burst Extends VHF Radio Range," *Aviation Week, 66* (June 17, 1957), 96.

C. A. Knight & Dean Fraser, "The Mutation of Viruses," *Scientific American, 193* (July 1955), 74.

Gerard P. Kuiper (ed.), *The Atmospheres of the Earth and Planets*, rev. ed., Chicago, University of Chicago, 1952.

W. S. S. Ladell, "The Myth About the Tropics," *UNESCO Courier, V* (July 1952), 4.

H. Landsberg, "The Origin of the Atmosphere," *Scientific American, 189* (August 1953), 82.

———, "Fire Storms Resulting from Bombing Conflagrations," *Bulletin of the American Meteorological Society, 28* (February 1947), 72.

Frank W. Lane, *The Elements Rage*, rev. ed., London, Country Life, 1948.

Irving Langmuir, *Widespread Control of Weather by Silver Iodide Seeding*, General Electric Co. Report No. 55–RL–1263, 1955.

Jonathan Norton Leonard, "Space, It's Enough to Make the Blood Boil," *Life, 35* (August 31, 1953), 91.

James E. Lett, "Noise, A Problem in Air Transport and in Ground Operation," *Aeronautical Engineering Review, 12* (April 1953), 65.

Willard F. Libby, "Radioactive Fallout," *Proceedings of the National Academy of Sciences, 43* (August 1957), 758.

———, "Radioactive Fallout and Radioactive Strontium," *Science, 123* (April 20, 1956), 657.

———, "Radiocarbon Dating," *American Scientists, 44* (Winter 1956), 98.

———, "Tritium in Nature," *Scientific American, 190* (April 1954), 38.

Urner Liddel, "Phantasmagoria or Unusual Observations in the Atmosphere," *Journal of the Optical Society of America, 43* (April 1953), 314.

Victor J. Linnenborn, "Radioactivity and the Age of the Earth," *Journal of Chemical Education, 32* (February 1955), 58.

William A. Long, "What's Happening to Our Glaciers!" *Scientific Monthly, 81* (August 1955), 57.

T. Morris Longstreth, *Understanding the Weather*, New York, Macmillan, 1953.

F. H. Ludlam, "The Structure of Rainclouds," *Weather, 11* (June 1956), 187.

——, "Artificial and Natural Shower Formation," *Weather, 7* (July 1952), 199.

R. A. Lyttleton, "On the Swerve of a Cricket Ball," *Weather, 12* (May 1957), 140.

Milton MacKaye, "We're Cracking the Secrets of Weather," *Saturday Evening Post, 227* (1954), Part I, September 11, 34; Part II, September 18, 36.

Paul L. Magill, Francis R. Holden, & Charles Ackley (eds.), *Air Pollution Handbook*, New York, McGraw-Hill, 1956.

Joanne Starr Malkus, "The Origin of Hurricanes," *Scientific American, 197* (August 1957), 33.

Thomas F. Malone (ed.), *Compendium of Meteorology*, Boston, American Meteorological Society, 1951.

S. F. Markham, *Climate and the Energy of Nations*, New York, Oxford University, 1957.

B. J. Mason, "Man's Influence on the Weather," *The Advancement of Science, 12* (June 1956), 498.

——, *The Physics of Clouds*, London, Oxford University Press, 1957.

——, "The Physics of Rain-Making," *Discovery, 16* (November 1955), 461.

James E. McDonald, "The Earth's Electricity," *Scientific American, 188* (April 1953), 32.

A. R. Meetham, *Atmospheric Pollution; Its Origins and Prevention*, London, Pergamon, 1952.

Donald H. Menzel, *Flying Saucers*, Cambridge, Harvard University, 1953.

Denning Duer Miller, *Wind, Storm, and Rain; the Story of Weather*, New York, Coward-McCann, 1952.

Lewis E. Miller, "Chemistry in the Stratosphere and Upper Atmosphere," *Journal of Chemical Education, 31* (March 1954), 112.

Stanley L. Miller, "Production of Some Organic Compounds Under Possible Primitive Earth Conditions," *Journal of the American Chemical Society, 77* (May 5, 1955), 2351.

M. Minnaert, *The Nature of Light & Colour in the Open Air*, New York, Dover, 1954.

S. Mitra, *The Upper Atmosphere,* 2nd. ed., Calcutta, Asiatic Society, 1952.

M. G. Morgan & G. McK. Allcock, "Observations of Whistling Atmospherics at Geomagnetically Conjugate Points," *Nature, 177* (January 1956), 29.

Forest R. Moulton (ed.), *Aerobiology,* Washington, American Association for the Advancement of Science, 1942.

Edwin Muller, "The Great London Fog," *Reader's Digest, 62* (May 1953), 25.

Guy Murchie, *Song of the Sky,* Cambridge, Riverside, 1954.

H. C. Murphy, "Control of Air Borne Organisms," *Heating, Piping and Air Conditioning, 10* (April 1938), 232.

Jerome Namias, "Long-Range Weather Forecasting," *Scientific American, 193* (August 1955), 40.

——, "The Jet Stream," *Scientific American, 187* (October 1952), 26.

Hans H. Neuberger, *Introduction to Physical Meteorology,* State College, Pa., Mineral Industries Extension Services, School of Mineral Industries, Pennsylvania State College, 1951.

John von Neumann, "Can We Survive Technology?" *Fortune, 51* (June 1955), 106.

H. B. Newcombe, "Magnitude of Biological Hazard from Strontium-90," *Science, 126* (September 20, 1957), 549.

——, *Population Risks from Radiations,* Atomic Energy of Canada Limited, Report No. 647, June 1958.

Homer E. Newell, "The Satellite Project," *Scientific American, 193* (December 1955), 29.

——, *High Altitude Rocket Research,* New York, Academic, 1953.

Edward P. Ney, "Heavy Elements from Space," *Scientific American, 184* (May 1951), 27.

B. C. V. Oddie, "The Meteorological Office Experiments on Artificial Rainfall," *Weather, 11* (March 1956), 65.

Mildred B. Oliver & Vincent J. Oliver, "Rainfall and Stardust," *Bulletin of the American Meteorological Society, 36* (April 1955), 147.

Ernst J. Öpik, "Climate and the Changing Sun," *Scientific American, 198* (June 1958), 85.

Clyde Orr, Jr., "Fine Particles," *Scientific American, 183* (December 1950), 53.

J. L. Orr, D. Fraser, & K. G. Petit, *Analysis of Experiments on Inducing Precipitation,* National Research Council of Canada, Report MD–32, August 17, 1949.

Howard T. Orville, "Weather Made to Order," *Collier's*, *133* (May 28, 1954), 25.

S. M. Pady & C. D. Kelly, "Numbers of Fungi and Bacteria in Transatlantic Air," *Science*, *117* (May 29, 1953), 607.

Hans A. Panofsky, "Theories of Climate Change," *Weatherwise*, *9* (December 1956), 183.

A. Parker, *The Destructive Effects of Air Pollution on Materials*, London, National Smoke Abatement Society, 1955.

James Paton, "Polar and Tropical Aurorae," *Endeavour*, *16* (January 1957), 42.

———, "Aurora Borealis," *Weather*, *1* (May 1946), 6.

Gerard Piel, "The Planet Earth," *Bulletin of the Atomic Scientists*, *11* (September 1955), 238.

Gilbert N. Plass, "Carbon Dioxide and Climate," *American Scientists*, *44* (July 1956), 302.

———, "The Carbon Dioxide Theory of Climatic Change," *Tellus*, *8* (May 1956), 140.

———, "Effect of Carbon Dioxide Variations on Climate," *American Journal of Physics*, *24* (May, 1956), 376.

James Poling, "Bomb-Dust Radiation!" *Better Homes & Gardens* (May 1957), 71.

Nicholas Polunin, S. M. Pady, & C. D. Kelly, "Arctic Aerobiology," *Nature*, *160* (December 20, 1947), 876.

S. E. Reynolds, M. Brook, & Mary Foulks Gourley, "Thunderstorm Charge Separation," *Journal of Meteorology*, *14* (October 1957), 426.

Walter Orr Roberts, "Can We Blame the Sun for Stormy Weather?" *Popular Mechanics*, *103* (June 1955), 65.

———, "Corpuscles from the Sun," *Scientific American*, *192* (February 1955), 40.

———, "Sun Clouds and Rain Clouds," *Scientific American*, *196* (April 1957), 138.

Wallace C. Sabine, *Collected Papers on Acoustics*, Cambridge, Harvard University, 1922.

Hermann J. Schaefer, "Exposure Hazards from Cosmic Radiation Beyond the Stratosphere and in Free Space," *Journal of Aviation Medicine*, *23* (August 1952), 334.

Vincent J. Schaefer, "Experimental Meteorology," *Journal of Applied Mathematics and Physics (Zamp)*, *1* (1950), 153.

———, "Thunderstorms and Project Skyfire," *Transactions of the New York Academy of Sciences*, Ser. 2 (April 1955), 470.

W. Schmitt, "Solar Eruptions & Stratospheric Weather," *Weather*, 7 (September 1952), 276.

B. F. J. Schonland, *Atmospheric Electricity*, 2nd. ed., rev., New York, Wiley, 1953.

———, *The Flight of Thunderbolts*, Oxford, Clarendon, 1950.

———, "The Work of Benjamin Franklin on Thunderstorms and the Development of the Lightning Rod," *Journal of the Franklin Institute*, 253 (May 1952), 375.

H. H. Schrenk, "Current Research on the Effects of Dusts," *Industrial and Engineering Chemistry*, 45 (August 1953), 111A.

Edmund Schulman, "Tree Rings and Climatic History," *Research Reviews* (September 1953), 1.

R. S. Scorer, "Condensation Trails," *Weather*, 10 (September 1955), 281.

Harlow Shapley (ed.), *Climatic Change*, Cambridge, Harvard University, 1953.

R. H. Simpson, "Hurricanes," *Scientific American*, 190 (June 1954), 32.

S. F. Singer, "Minimum Earth Satellites as 'Storm Patrol'," *Scientific Monthly*, 85 (August 1957), 95.

Lyman Spitzer, Jr., "Horizons in Astronomy," *American Scientist*, 43 (Spring 1955), 323.

Victor P. Starr, "The General Circulation of the Atmosphere," *Scientific American*, 195 (December 1956), 40.

L. R. O. Storey, "Whistlers," *Scientific American*, 194 (January 1956), 34.

C. G. Suits, "Man-Made Weather," *Journal of the Franklin Institute*, 254 (July 1952), 99.

R. C. Sutcliffe, "Rain: Natural and Artificial," *British Journal of Applied Physics*, 7 (March 1956), 85.

W. F. G. Swann, "The Present Status of Atmospheric Electricity," *Journal of the Franklin Institute*, 260 (October 1955), 283.

J. M. Talbot, "Breaking the Sound Barrier and Its Effect on the Public," *Journal of the American Medical Association*, 158 (August 27, 1955), 1508.

Morris Tepper, "Tornadoes," *Scientific American*, 198 (May 1958), 31.

W. C. Turner, "Atmospheric Pollution," *Weather*, 10 (April 1955), 110.

Harold C. Urey, *The Planets, Their Origin and Development*, New Haven, Yale University, 1952.

R. G. Veryard, "Some Thoughts on Climatic Change," *Weather*, 11 (November 1956), 355.

Bernard Vonnegut & Charles B. Moore, "Electrical Activity Associated with the Blackwell-Udall Tornado," *Journal of Meteorology*, 14 (June 1957), 284.

Alden H. Waitt, *Gas Warfare, the Chemical Weapon; Its Use, and Protection Against It*, New York, Duell, Sloan and Pearce, 1942.

Helmut Weickmann & Waldo Smith (eds.), *Artificial Stimulation of Rain*, New York, Pergamon, 1957.

William F. Wells, *Airborne Contagion and Air Hygiene: An Ecological Study of Droplet Infections*, Cambridge, Harvard University, 1955.

William H. Wenstrom, *Weather and the Ocean of Air*, Boston, Houghton Mifflin, 1942.

Frits W. Went, "Air Pollution," *Scientific American, 192* (May 1955), 62.

———, "Climate and Agriculture," *Scientific American, 196* (June 1957), 82.

Harry Wexler, "Meteorology in the International Geophysical Year," *Scientific Monthly, 84* (March 1957), 141.

———, "On the Effects of Volcanic Dust on Insolation and Weather," *Bulletin of the American Meteorological Society, 32* (January 1951), 10.

———, "Volcanoes and World Climate," *Scientific American, 186* (April 1952), 74.

Fred L. Whipple, "The Coming Exploration in Space," *Saturday Evening Post, 231* (August 16, 1958), 33.

Clayton S. White & Otis O. Benson, Jr. (eds.), *Physics and Medicine of the Upper Atmosphere*, Albuquerque, University of New Mexico, 1952.

Leigh White, "That Creeping Menace Called Smog," *Saturday Evening Post, 229* (May 4, 1957), 34.

Jerome B. Wiesner, "New Method of Radio Transmission," *Scientific American, 196* (January 1957), 46.

Verne O. Williams, "Can Rain Makers Really Make Rain?" *Saturday Evening Post, 224* (December 1, 1951), 26.

A. H. Woodstock, "Salt and Rain," *Scientific American, 197* (October 1957), 42.

Frederick R. Wulsin, "Hot Weather and High Achievement," *Florida Anthropologist, 5* (December 1953), 103.

A. M. Zarem & W. E. Rand, "Smog," *Scientific American, 186* (May 1952), 15.

M. Zelikoff (ed.), *The Threshold of Space*, New York, Pergamon, 1957.

——— & others, "An Attempt to Measure Atomic Nitrogen by Rocket Release of Ethylene at 105 and 143 KM," *Journal of Geophysical Research, 63* (March 1958), 31.

index